Free *and* Unequal

*F*ree *and* Unequal

The Biological Basis *of* Individual Liberty

By Roger J. Williams

AUSTIN : UNIVERSITY OF TEXAS PRESS : 1953

UNIVERSITY OF TEXAS PRESS
Austin 12

THOMAS NELSON AND SONS LTD
Parkside Works Edinburgh 9
3 Henrietta Street London WC2
312 Flinders Street Melbourne C1
5 Parker's Buildings Burg Street Cape Town

Thomas Nelson and Sons (Canada) Ltd
91–93 Wellington Street West Toronto 1

Société Française d'Editions Nelson
25 rue Henri Barbusse Paris Ve

Library of Congress Catalog Card Number 53-5997

Manufactured in the United States of America

To the memory of
Hazel
who, faced by ill health,
unselfishly gave her life
for those she loved the best

Acknowledgments

I WISH TO ACKNOWLEDGE my grateful thanks to all those who have helped, by encouragement or by generous performance, to make possible the early completion of this book. Among those who have critically read all or parts of the manuscript and have made valuable suggestions are Dean A. P. Brogan, University of Texas; Professors J. P. Nafe, Washington University, St. Louis; H. H. Strandskov, University of Chicago, and DeWitt Reddick, University of Texas; Drs. Lorene L. Rogers, University of Texas; W. K. Livingston, University of Oregon Medical School; R. R. Williams, Summit, N. J., and Clay Palmer, Bloomington, California; Messrs. Frank H. Wardlaw, University of Texas Press; Dale T. Wood, Vista, California, and Roger J. Williams, Jr., Falls Church, Va.

Particular thanks are due to Mrs. Kathleen Sproul of New York for her able editorial assistance throughout, and for excellent criticisms and suggestions.

For the mistakes or misjudgments which may be manifest in the final volume, I take the full responsibility—none of those who aided should be blamed for anything connected with its contents. If readers will call my attention to errors, or offer constructive suggestions with respect to the contents of this book, their acts of kindness will be appreciated.

ROGER J. WILLIAMS

Contents

To My Readers

When acquaintances have asked me what this book is about, I have been unable to give them the quick and concise answer I could have given if I had been writing on some restricted phase of biochemistry, the field of my training and experience. While this book does not deal with any branch of biochemistry, nevertheless that subject has a considerable bearing on its central theme.

This book has to do, for example, with the fact that a strong contingent of socially-minded Americans apparently agree, unfortunately, with the Soviet dictators on one point: that so far as the human scene is concerned, genetics (and this includes biochemical genetics) may as well be banished from our thinking. The Russians have made their position on this point clear by liquidating Vavilov and other free-thinking geneticists and have enthroned those who "think right." We Americans have been led to take, almost as definitely, a parallel position alongside the Soviets by deliberately or at best unintentionally *ignoring* the facts of genetics as they bear upon our political thinking. We may pay lip service to the fact that children are born different—each one an individual—but we do virtually nothing about it. We go our way and develop many of our basic social theories as though they were all essentially alike.

When one mentions the word genetics, it inevitably brings to some people's minds the idea of setting up a program of human breeding which will improve the race. This is certainly *not* what I am advocating. I am not concerned with getting better or different people by human breeding; I am concerned with the basic problem of human life today, *understanding the people we already have!*

When we are dealing with cattle or horses, dogs or cats, wheat, corn, or cotton, we accept the facts of genetics as axiomatic and make tremendous use of them. When we are concerned with people, we put up a bar in our thinking. We say, "No! Babies are born 'normal' and must remain so; men must be interchangeable parts in society."

The central theme of this volume evolves out of asking, and answering, a very simple question, but its development results in opening up new vistas in the fields of education, medicine, art, religion, and politics—in fact, with respect to every phase of life. It is as though we were explorers approaching, without the aid of aircraft, a completely unknown land which is protected from inquisitive strangers by a high wall, impregnable except for a single small unprotected opening. Clearly, the small opening will be, as we approach, the central point of interest. Once we have reached the focal point and have decided to pass through the entrance, the diverse findings immediately available to sight on the other side become so much more interesting than the passageway that we may even forget we ever came through it.

The concepts and conclusions dealt with in this book are distilled from a tremendous mass of evidence and experience, much of it originally highly technical and stemming from the general field of biology and more specifically from the fields of physiology, biochemistry, psychology, and genetics. However, this is not a scientific book in the sense that the technical evidence is assembled and organized bit by bit and the conclusions drawn when the evidence is all in. Such a book is usually, to lay readers, tedious in detail and hedged about as to conclusions; such a book might serve as a textbook to determined readers, but it would not reach the general readers to whom I hope the ideas I have set forth will prove potent and stimulating if not revolutionary.

Yet, in another sense, this *is* a scientific book, for the recently developed basic concepts on which its conclusions rest are wholly accepted scientifically. These concepts have been discussed with a considerable number of the most competent experts in universities and institutes here and abroad—at Pasadena, Berkeley, Madison, Chicago,

Cambridge (Massachusetts), New York, Cambridge (England), Amsterdam, Delft, Utrecht, Zurich, Copenhagen, Stockholm, Uppsala. I have not found among these anyone who differed in opinion on any scientific matter pertinent to the basic material here presented.

Down through the ages our thinking about humanity and human problems has failed to encompass certain far-reaching ideas, the truth of which, on the basis of recent accumulation of evidence, cannot be denied. It is with these ideas and truths and their broad and potent implications that this book is concerned.

Free and Unequal

I

The Question

THE QUESTION that is crucial to the theme of this book is a simple one. But the reader should be warned that simple questions may be profound and may hold complex implications. The answer cannot be snapped out of the air as a trout snaps at a fly, for it requires careful inquiry and deliberate thought. Stated in its simplest form, the question is: *Are newborn babies essentially uniform products?*

At first sight this may seem an unexciting query. A reader may even have an answer immediately at hand and assume that everyone else would agree with his ready-made reply. However, there is actually a wide divergence of opinion on this subject, and it is a basic matter which colors (probably more than we suspect) much of our reasoning about, and many of our attitudes toward, matters as varied as education, business, Communism, the welfare state, and so on. And it is emphatically not a closed question. In recent years, indeed in recent months, new explorations have thrown light on it and on the broader problem of human nature to which it inevitably leads.

Let us suppose that one (perhaps a follower of John B. Watson) is disposed to answer the question in the affirmative, in which case he may first remind us that our forefathers stated explicitly in the Declaration of Independence, "We hold these truths to be self-evident, that all men are created . . . equal . . ." and that equality is therefore recognized as the handmaiden of democracy. He could tell us that it seems to him that our democratic system is based upon the fact that children *do* come into the world substantially alike, each one the equal of others in the sight of God and in the eyes of the state. But as he goes on talking, it becomes apparent that he is not defending the opinion that children are uniform as much as he is telling us why it is convenient to assume that they are.

He might point out that, if the world is made up of human beings all more or less alike in their capacities, education becomes a lever that can lift the world. Do not most educators believe that, if you surround children through training with the proper social environment, social stresses and evils will eventually be eliminated? If we can be molded by education, the unification of the human race seems a realizable dream; and every mother has a right to believe, he insists, that her child has a potentiality for greatness equal to that of every neighbor's child, his future depending only on the associations with which she is able to surround him. Besides, he says, young people growing up need the hope that a belief in a boundless potentiality alone can give them. If they are thought of at birth as being books with similar blank pages, each capable of being filled similarly with great knowledge and value, they will not give up trying and their optimism will never be dimmed. The successes attained in pursuing these goals prove, our affirmer says, that the human race is truly remarkable. Our respect for human capabilities should be great.

It is easy enough to understand why this imaginary speaker, who would be representative of many, feels that the influences of environment (including education) are so great. Environment is of course clearly subject to modification; but when it comes to helping an individual person or advancing the status of a group it is obvious that nothing can be done in the way of changing grandfathers or grandmothers. The only help, then, seems to lie in altering environment, since hereditary factors are obscure and appear to be in the laps of the gods.

But now let us suppose that someone answers the initial question in the negative. He may first say that the "free and equal" phrase in the Declaration of Independence was an unfortunate paraphrase of a better statement contained in the Virginia Bill of Rights, antedating the Declaration by about three weeks. In the earlier document the statement reads, "all men are by nature equally free and independent." In other words, men can be *equally free* without being *uniform,* and the supporter of the negative suspects the founding fathers meant that people should be treated as equals regardless of station in life, that no one should be discriminated against because of any accident of birth, that each should be given equal rights before the law and equal opportunity to demonstrate his worth.

He may also say that education is all the more important if children are *not* alike and that education's great task is to help them find their distinctive endowments and train them accordingly. He may in addition ask some rather disconcerting questions, such as: "Does not our love of liberty, which seems to be inherent in all of us, rest squarely upon our *in*equalities? If at birth we all possessed the same potential tastes with respect to the stuff of life—food, drink, art, music, books, love, religion, learning—would we care about being free to pursue them as we individually desire? If we could be trained to do any kind of work, would it matter what we did, or that work might be assigned to us as someone else saw fit?"

And as to babies, he might say, "Suppose that each baby is a replica of all others—does not the life of the individual child lose significance? If the next specimen on the assembly line is substantially a duplicate of the one before it, individual worth is almost obsolete, or at best trivial." And it may be fine, he remarks, to present young people with the idea of an "infinite potentiality," but how about the frustration of ambition-driven youths who do try but fail to live up to supposedly infinite possibilities? And what of the bitterness in parents who note that their children's performance is mediocre or worse and who must blame themselves for not having supplied the environment which should have allowed their offspring to live supremely well?

As you may have deduced from the title of this book, the answer to our key question was already settled in the author's mind before the book was written. The reader may recognize that the question is related to the time-honored and, in a sense, outworn debate regarding the relative importance of heredity and environment in making people what they are. But the crucial matter that I am discussing and the one on which people—and scholars—do not agree is not the relative importance of heredity and environment but whether or not heredity is worthy of consideration as a practical and fundamental social factor.

Debate as to the fundamental importance of anything without ample facts on which to base arguments is fruitless, and the question of the relative importance of environment and heredity is, according to modern biological concepts, essentially unanswerable. We might as well ask which is more fundamental to the development of a chick, a *fertilized egg* or a *suitable temperature* to hatch it. In the absence of either fertilized egg or suitable temperature, the chick never happens! In biology it is never heredity *versus* environment or nature *versus* nurture; these factors always work together.

I am convinced that the question posed is one of basic importance and that our answer to it can determine to a large degree how we will meet many public problems on which we find frequent and pointed disagreement. I have thought about the "doctrine of uniformity" and its antithesis from many angles over a period of years. This thinking, reading, and researching on the specific subject of human variation (certain results of which were given in my book *The Human Frontier*) backed by decades of experience in the biological field, has left no shred of doubt in my mind. The uniformity theory is wholly untenable. The evidence for nonuniformity—and I mean important nonuniformity—is so vast and overwhelming that it would be a subterfuge for me to pretend to ignore my biological background and play at facing the problem *de novo*. In the earlier book some of the evidence was set forth, and since then my colleagues and I have worked on further research leading to still more evidence. But in this present volume the evidence will be touched on only lightly, for it is the application of it to our social scene that now seems important to me and that, in a sense, constitutes the actual proof of the pudding.

Basic thinking on questions as momentous as this influences our lives greatly whether we recognize it or not. A young man entering matrimony does not usually go through the process of consciously outlining his theory of marriage or of the nature of womankind. *He has a theory* nonetheless, and the success of his marriage will depend materially on what the theory is. When couples start the job of rearing a child, they do not write down in the baby book their theory of child development. *Each has a theory* nonetheless, and everything done or not done for the child is a resultant, in substantial part, of their ideas about how children grow up. Everyone who has anything to do with an infant or a child, in school or out, acts in accordance with his ideas, often accepted tacitly and at second hand, of what children are like and how they develop. In all of our dealings with people we make use, whether consciously or not, of our basic ideas about the nature of humankind and why we behave as we do. But the basic ideas may not be the result of real thinking; they may lack soundness because they have not been personally tested and because they have been imbibed as random hearsay.

In our concern with public problems we tend to dwell too much upon immediate issues and events (about which we are likely to grow overheated) and to let the fundamental principles go hang. It is possible that our body politic has deep-seated diseases and that our tendency to get overheated is itself a symptom of disease. We cannot cure the physical disease syphilis by superficial treatment of the sores it produces, and it is possible that dangerous political and social diseases need far more basic treatment than they receive.

This is not an academic book concerned with abstruse or philosophical questions. The questions we wish to consider are practical ones: Are newborn babies sufficiently alike so that we need pay little or no attention to their differences? Should our everyday lives, our educational systems, our political activities, our attitudes toward art, religion, and each other be built upon the assumption that we are more or less uniform? Or can we, on the other hand, by noting and understanding *in*-equalities solve human problems that seem otherwise insoluble?

Because it can easily be seen that environments are capable of modification, the study of environmental effects in human development has been undertaken from many viewpoints by many natural scientists and by scholars in the fields of social and educational psychology, sociology, and social anthropology. Studies by anthropologists have gone a long way toward producing a comprehensive and convincing picture of what cultures can do, and have done, to and for people. The "culture concept" has evolved and is regarded by experts in the field as a milestone in human understanding and the key to further advance.

The study of heredity as it relates directly to the problems of humanity has been limited largely to the medical field, and even in this area has not been conspicuously stressed—for instance, it was not until 1949 that the American Society of Human Genetics and the *Journal of Human Genetics* were founded. What heredity may have to do with our daily activities—eating, sleeping, working, playing, reading, thinking—has received very little consideration at anyone's hands.

In view of the complications involved in tracing the action of genes in mammalian heredity and the fact that there is far more than enough in this specialized area to occupy the total labors of the available geneticists, the blame for neglect of heredity as a factor in our daily lives cannot fairly be laid at their doorstep. After all, they have been trained and employed as specialists in genetics. If they become interested in human beings—as many of them actually are—this interest must be subordinated as a sideline.

As a result of this tendency toward environmentally-centered thinking and investigation, the doctrine of the essential uniformity of human infants has been widely accepted and is held by a great body of social psychologists, sociologists, social anthropologists, and many others, including historians, economists, educationalists, legal scholars, and men in public life. The doctrine has been incorporated into the prevailing mode of thought of many who have to do with shaping educational and governmental policies and is often accepted unquestioningly by those who do little critical thinking of their own.

Yet, in spite of this general tendency, it is significant that each individual, even though he may not question the doctrine when tacitly applied to all other men, seems to have an instinctive feeling that *he* is unique and resists the acknowledgment of uniformity when applied to *himself*. And it is also true that the uniformity idea in its boldest form is not usually *actively* promulgated; it is more often tacitly assumed to be acceptable and true; at least activities are carried on as if it were true and the allowances that should be made for the fact of human variation are not made. If the experts who hold this doctrine were asked point blank, many of them would speak a few polite words for the heredity factor. In spite of themselves they must recognize that "constitutional factors" are real in human life, and that human beings are what they are because of nature *and* nurture. Yet, in their professional writings, in their investigations of social problems, and in the applications they make of their over-all thinking, hereditary and constitutional factors are neglected as though wholly unimportant.

One variant of the doctrine, not openly avowed but to be inferred from current writings, admits that babies as born do differ somewhat from each other, but that they are sufficiently adaptable so they can be made uniform by cultural influences. This of course maintains the essence of the general doctrine.

The question is emphatically not academic. I believe we can say that *it is the basic one that underlies the predominant ideological conflict in the world today*. Other fundamental questions are related to it: Can human beings be educated to be regimented by any agency—industry, the state, or any other—or are they by nature each one distinctive, thus requiring liberty to develop, each in his own individual way? Is there any better basis for promoting our freedom than by understanding the differences between men?

As our populations have grown, as industry and commerce have established mass markets for products and services, as communications have put peoples intimately in touch with each other from one end of the world to the other, the trend of civilization, particularly in our own country, has seemed to be toward more and more "collective sameness." Marketable goods are gauged for a mass of buyers (if you have an individual preference in some product, it is often difficult to satisfy it); education is geared in our huge universities for a mass of students, with all the uniformity of rules and regulations which handling a crowd entails (if you have individual excellences or difficulties, the statistics will iron them out); industry is dependent on the assembly line (and the craftsman who could take pride in his production of a total piece of work must subordinate this skill); entertainment tends to be poured out of Hollywood for all men alike—and now out of television studios. Thus in the midst of lip service paid to individualism, many affairs of our daily lives are conducted as if human differences were only minor decorations on the cake, not to be seriously considered in the "realistic" business of life. True realism, however, would heed the individual differences, needs, and desires of human beings, recognizing the fact that frustrations, discontents, breakdowns, and even wars may arise out of their neglect.

The totalitarian ideologies that have made such tragic difficulties for the world in the last few decades represent, I believe, the ultimate result of the uniformity doctrine—I do not say the ultimate triumph, because I am sure that they will always fail since they rest on the sand of a false premise. Karl Marx, like most social theorists, appeared not to consider heredity as a factor to be dealt with, though it should be said to his credit that he yearned for freedom and imagined that eventually the state would wither away and liberty for men to manage their own affairs would emerge. Those in the Soviet Union, however, who profess to be followers of Marx (and they are followers in only a limited way) have virtually destroyed the science of genetics within their borders and have become out-and-out environmentalists. According to Soviet practice, people do not need freedom; they need to be regimented; they need to follow *the plan;* the best citizen is he who is best at taking orders. Testing human aptitudes, for instance, to determine what an individual might be best fitted for is entirely contrary to the prevailing mode of thought in Russia, and I am informed on the basis of personal observation, that it simply isn't done.

The importance of the uniformity idea in the Soviet scheme of things is demonstrated by the fact that the related scientific findings have become a political issue. Vavilov and other famous geneticists who stood by their findings have been liquidated, and Lysenko, who has become a propagandist for environmentalism, has been elevated to leadership. One does not know whether the powers-that-be of the Soviet completely realize how essential Lysenko's doctrine is to their total scheme; but one suspects they do know that if the importance of human differences were to be stressed, a Pandora's box of troubles for their regime would be opened, leading to inevitable downfall.

Our basic question is one that requires a yes or no answer; there can be no hedging. If the differences which exist between us at birth are *un*-important or easily expunged, we may say for practical purposes that we are uniform. But if the differences are important *in any way,* the uniformity idea collapses. If we take the position that the differences are unimportant, then we force ourselves into supporting the idea that liberty is at best unimportant, unneeded, and of minor significance. In this case Patrick Henry was being pigheaded and fanatic when he said, "Give me liberty or give me death," and all the other men down through history who have tenaciously sought freedom have been led astray by a false ideal.

Further, if we conclude that babies differ from each other only in inconsequential ways, we are forced to accept another corollary: One baby could be substituted for another without substantial loss, and there is no consequential basis for regarding the life of any one child as distinctly valuable.

There is no middle ground; *distinctiveness, individual worth, and freedom rise or fall together.* If we choose to believe that distinctiveness is important only in certain areas of existence, then we have said in effect that individual worth is also important only in these areas and liberty is desirable only within these areas. It is a matter, it seems to me, which we must all face squarely. As one who is a scientist by training and inclination, I have faced it and have been prepared to take the consequences of my decision. If "Americanism," as I have been led to think of it, is built upon the sand—a false idea of human nature—I would abandon it and build upon a sound foundation! But actually a study of the question, instead of raising doubts about the fundamental ideals of liberty and individual worth, has tremendously strengthened my belief in their validity and has clarified and deepened the basis for this belief.

I believe that the basic question here set forth has received, unfortunately, little attention or thought from those who are interested in human welfare and in public affairs. Yet when it is faced in the light of all its implications (which hitherto has never happened) its crucial nature will be recognized, and the one answer which squares with the scientific facts will be accepted with unanimity. We must deal with humanity *as it is,* and this includes its tremendous variability.

If men and women were the products of an assembly-line creation, the state or any other agency could successfully tell them what they are to hear, to read, to say, to do, to worship, to think. But efforts toward such regimentation have never been successful; forcing people into a common pattern has always only resulted in the one cry that does seem universal to men: "Freedom!"

Ignoring the facts of human variability, we have talked far too glibly about *man,* an abstraction that implies uniformity, and have understood, and sought to understand, far too little about *men.* We have been unrealistic when we have planned for this hypothetical abstraction; we should be learning about the tremendous variations of the people who actually inhabit our planet, so that we can plan on the basis of the needs those variations entail.

Even in our non-Soviet culture much of our social, economic, and political thinking and planning is based (unfortunately, I believe) upon a tacit acceptance of the assembly-line doctrine of human nature, or a reasonable facsimile thereof. It is for this reason, or at least partly so, that many think they see a consistent drift toward the acceptance of what are currently called Communistic or near-Communistic ideas.

Biology completely vindicates the idea which was back of the pronouncement in the Virginia Bill of Rights: "All men are by nature equally free and independent." Biology reveals no "right" of kings to govern, no "royal blood." There is no genetic advantage in being born under affluent circumstances. Human worth and even potential greatness may appear anywhere. A backwoods baby born to unprosperous parents, possessing nothing of what we call culture, may turn out to be an Abraham Lincoln. A puny, sickly one, born in an obscure village and having a threadlike hold on life, may result in a Mark Twain. An infant who loses sight and hearing during babyhood may turn out to be the magnificent specimen of humanity that Helen Keller is. Actually human worth resides not only in those whom we regard as great, but in all of us, and we should provide an environment which will give everyone an *equal chance* to develop his potentialities in the way best suited to him individually.

It seems to me clear that the idea of freedom arose directly out of this human variability. If we were all alike there would seem to be no reason for wanting freedom; "living my own life" would be an empty, meaningless expression. True, we are alike as *human beings*, and have a common role to play in the world, but among the infinite number of ways to play the role we crave the liberty of our own choices.

One of the prime functions of this book is to examine various areas of life to see where distinctiveness plays an important part and where it does not. We can then see where individual worth and liberty are most significant and where they are less so. The full answer must await further extensive investigation and study, but we can make a start. I must state that to me the facts of human variability, as I have seen them, constitute a firm foundation for our conceived ideal of democracy and that vacillation or lukewarmness about the principles of freedom and human worth appears preposterous in the light of the evidence. I believe these ideals came into being because people are *what they are*—creatures possessing high variability—and that therefore the ideals are impregnable.

II

Human Animals

THE GREEK PHILOSOPHER Theophrastus expressed in a refreshing way over two thousand years ago his curiosity about the people around him. He found people just as diverse in their inclinations as we find them today and wrote a book about the various types of characters, as he saw them. On the first page of the book he said: "Many a time ere now I have stopped to think and wonder—I fancy the marvel will never grow less—why it is that we Greeks are not all one in character, for we have the same climate throughout the country and our people enjoy the same education."

To one who is acquainted with the fundamental principles of biology—and takes them seriously—an immediate answer to Theophrastus' query comes to mind. How about biological variability as an explanation?

To talk of human beings and their characteristics as related to biology means that we regard them as members of the biological kingdom. It is manifestly true that man does belong on a higher plane than animals; he has demonstrated this through the process of social inheritance. We are able, for example, to think after Theophrastus the thoughts that he entertained many centuries ago. No animal is able to do anything comparable. To think of human beings as belonging to the animal kingdom (we certainly are not plants) is not, however, to consider them as lacking higher attributes. We would not wish to say that they are *merely* animals.

As biological specimens, human beings are closely related physically, as is well known, to other mammals, and much that we know about the human body we have learned indirectly by studying experimental animals. One cannot be informed, even in a fragmentary way, regarding the facts of biology without recognizing the comprehensive unity which exists. Regardless of just how we may conceive the biological world or human beings to have arisen, we cannot look at living things without appreciating that all organisms are related to each other—some distantly, some closely. Human beings represent the highest form of life, since they possess the inherent attributes of all the lower forms, plus attributes of their own which transcend those exhibited by animals.

Just as animals are more and more complex the higher they are in the biological scale, so we find that *individuality*, a matter with which we are greatly concerned, is progressively more highly developed as the scale ascends.

The relative lack of individuality in lower forms of life is easily demonstrated. In the lower invertebrates, hydroids and planarian worms, parts of different animals can be grafted together with complete success; no antagonism develops, the two parts coalescing to produce a perfect whole. In earthworms which are a little higher, similar grafting experiments involving two different earthworms are successful provided the segments are all pointed in the same direction, that is, from head to tail. If a single earthworm is cut into three segments and grafted back together again, the middle segment can be put in the wrong end to without any difficulty, but if the middle segment is from a second worm and is put in the wrong way, the graft will not take. This appears to be the beginning of individuality.

In frogs which are higher in the scale than the invertebrates, we find unmistakable signs of individuality. If a bit of skin is taken from one portion of a frog and transplanted to another area, the graft will grow and the transplant remains indefinitely. If, however, a bit of frog skin is transplanted in the same way to another frog of the same species, the graft may or may not grow. In chameleons, skin transplants from other chameleons heal in and then are absorbed two or three months later, whereas a skin transplant from one portion of a chameleon to another part of the same animal heals in and is never absorbed. Frogs and chameleons possess a certain degree of individuality.

In birds and mammals, which are higher in the biological scale, individuality is much more marked. In these forms transplantation of skin from one portion of the body to another portion is readily made, but as soon as one attempts to transplant skin from one animal to another, complications arise. In general the difficulties involved in transplanting skin and other tissues from one individual mammal to another depend upon the closeness of the relationship between the two animals. If the two animals involved are of the same species, but not directly related, the difficulties appear sooner than if the two animals are related as brother-sister or father-son. If the parents of offspring are themselves closely related and are the result of inbreeding for many generations, transplantation from one of the offspring to another is relatively permanent and successful. In no case, however, will the tissues from another animal fit perfectly into the body of the host animal, and remain indefinitely thoroughly coordinated. In this sense each rat is an individual rat distinguishable from all others, and every guinea pig is a distinctly individual guinea pig.

While in human beings it is possible to transplant certain nonindividualistic tissues such as nasal cartilage or the cornea of the eye from one individual to another, tissue transplantations in general are unsuccessful. Blood is not highly individualistic and can be transfused in selected cases, depending on blood groupings. Skin transplantation has a long history. Transplantation from one part of a person's body to another part is uniformly successful, but with the possible exception of identical twins, transplantations from one person to another are not successful in man except for the most temporary covering of a burned area.

A case of a mother donating skin to her severely burned child during the recent world war will illustrate. In addition to being the mother she had the seeming advantage of belonging to the same blood group and having the same Rh factor. Yet the grafts grew only a few days, then broke down and sloughed off. Repeated grafts behaved in the same manner except that the "takes" were progressively less successful. The third time the grafts were applied they broke down almost immediately—the child's body had been building up antibodies to counteract and eliminate the foreign proteins in the mother's skin.

Leo Loeb, who made a life study of biological individuality, said in speaking of the broad field of biology, "We find, phylogenetically, a progressively increasing complexity in the activities of organisms and increasing differences between members of the same species, an increasing *individualization* which reaches its *highest development in man.*" (Italics mine.)

There are those who for various reasons like to think that the gap between humans and animals is a wide one. They point out how parallels between human beings and animals fail because so many human activities are influenced by *culture* (something that passes down by printed and recited words, by works of art, music, etc., from generation to generation) whereas for animals no comparable influence exists.

Thinking biologically and admitting that the gap between animals and man is tremendous, is there anyone who would be inclined to say: "Biological variability becomes progressively more distinct in the higher forms of animal life, but in man there is a reversion to the lower forms, and individuality disappears"? This is the position which the uniformity theory seems to demand.

The gap between higher animals and man surely is in the direction of more individuality, not less. Much biological evidence can be cited to support this conclusion.

The ways in which human beings exhibit marked individuality are literally so numerous as to be overwhelming. Any attempt to mention them all would lead inevitably to important omissions. In my book *The Human Frontier* many of these have been brought together for the first time, and the cumulative evidence has been impressive especially to the many who were informed only regarding certain areas.

Individuals differ from each other even in the minutest details of anatomy and body chemistry and physics: finger and toe prints; microscopic texture of hair; hair pattern on the body; ridges and "moons" on the finger and toe nails; thickness of skin, its color, its tendency to blister; distribution of nerve endings on the surface of the body; size and shape of ears, of ear canals, of semicircular canals; length of fingers; character of brain waves (tiny electrical impulses given off by the brain); exact number of muscles in the body; heart action; strength of blood vessels; blood groups; rate of clotting of blood—and so on almost *ad infinitum*.

A considerable number of such items have been investigated from the standpoint of genetics, and the mode of inheritance has been reasonably well established. The more detailed the genetic studies are, the more complicated the findings become (for example, there are three sets of genes which determine finger print patterns) and while the mode of inheritance may be difficult to work out in many cases, the fact of inheritance is indubitable. No informed person could have the slightest doubt that red hair (or more precisely, the chemical mechanism which produces red hair) is inherited, and yet the mode of inheritance is not at all well established.

One of the most striking recently discovered evidences of individuality concerns salivas. Geneticists became interested nearly twenty years ago in a chemical, phenyl thiocarbamide, which is bitter to some individuals and tasteless to others. The mode of inheritance of this taste difference is well established. Very recently, however, it has been found that a person to whom this chemical tastes intensely bitter is not able to taste it unless it is dissolved in his own saliva. If it is placed directly upon the dry tongue, no taste registers; if it is dissolved in water and placed upon the dry tongue, no taste is discerned; if it is dissolved in *anyone else's* saliva and tested in the same way, the results again are nil. However, when the chemical is dissolved *in one's own saliva* and then a drop is placed upon the dry tongue in the same way, the result is an extremely bitter taste! Biologically speaking, it would be absurd to imagine that inheritance involves only minutiae or that the sum of all the items is nothing of consequence. Actually the attribute of being human must come by inheritance; it never happens to dogs or pigeons or snails.

Most of the items showing individuality mentioned in an earlier paragraph were those that can be observed readily since they involve the surface of the body. When we go deeper into our insides, we find individuality there too, but of course study of this sort is less convenient and hence less extensive, since it must often be done *post mortem.*

The endocrine glands of each individual are different and distinctive. Among so-called normal individuals the thyroid glands vary in weight from 8 grams up to 50 grams, and there can be no doubt but that the size and activity of one's thyroid glands make a difference. Too great a deficiency will cause one to be a cretin idiot, and there are all degrees of deficiency. Excess thyroid causes severe trouble, too. The size of one's thyroid is determined largely by heredity just as is the size of one's ears or one's feet. Animals with large thyroids and animals with small thyroids have been produced at will by inbreeding, proving that heredity is involved.

Of course environmental factors influence the size and activity of one's thyroid gland too. If there is iodine deficiency in the food, the glands may swell up greatly but still they can't do their work. There are other nutritional substances besides iodine which may also have an effect. The fact remains that even when people supplement their iodine intake by using iodized salt, and consume ordinary foods, the thyroid glands of different individuals differ markedly in size and activity.

When the condition of too great or too little activity of the thyroid is recognized, the fact that it may have a hereditary origin does not prevent remedying the situation so far as that particular individual is concerned. In the case of too great activity surgery or other means may be used; in case the activity is too little, taking thyroid tissue or its equivalent by mouth will make up for the deficiency. These measures would not influence the size or activity of the thyroids of the subsequently conceived children of the treated individuals. There are doubtless a great many people who are mildly deficient in thyroid hormone and would be benefited by taking it orally, but they are not ill enough to see a physician or to submit to a careful diagnosis.

Of the many glands in the body the pituitary is the most complicated both as to structure and functions. Its different parts produce different hormones and are made up of different assortments of cell types. The glands are small, about the size of a pea, and are said to vary in over-all weight in males from 350 to 800 milligrams. In women they are somewhat larger and increase somewhat in size with each succeeding pregnancy. In the case of this gland we cannot speak broadly of "overactivity" or "underactivity" because a considerable number of hormones are produced and a particular pituitary gland may be overactive with respect to some hormones, underactive with respect to others, and average with respect to the remainder. There is good reason to believe that, so far as producing individual hormones is concerned, there is wide variation from gland to gland in different normal individuals.

That the size, shape, cellular make-up, etc., of pituitary glands is determined to a large extent by heredity is indicated by the fact that experimental animals with small pituitaries or with large pituitaries can be produced by selective inbreeding. Mice have been produced by experimental breeding which are practically lacking in the type of cells (acidophiles) which produce the "growth hormone." As a result of this inherited inability to produce the growth hormone, the mice are dwarfs. If these mice are administered the growth hormone (obtained from the pituitaries of other full-sized animals) by injection, they grow to normal size—they are no longer of dwarf size. From the genetic standpoint, however, they are still dwarfs and are unable to produce offspring with pituitaries containing the acidophile cells. The progeny will still be dwarfs.

Dwarfism in animals and in human beings is often caused by insufficient production of growth hormone by the pituitary gland, and the stature of every individual is determined in part by the make-up of his inherited pituitary gland. If nutrition is inadequate (this is of course environmental) stunting may result regardless of one's pituitary.

Control of body size in human individuals who tend to be of small stature would presumably be possible if growth hormone administration were instituted at the right time. However, the growth hormone cannot be produced artificially and is not available in suitable quantities. A general appreciation of biological variability and of the fact that body size is not a measure of worth would help to dispel the worries of some people in this connection.

Prolactin, another hormone produced by the pituitary, has profound psychological as well as physiological effects when administered to experimental animals. It not only causes virgin rats to produce milk but gives them a tremendous urge to mother love. If baby rats are placed in a cage with a virgin female, she will ordinarily pay no attention whatever to them. If, however, she is injected with prolactin, she will soon take an interest in them. She will prepare a nest for them, carry them to it, and suckle them. The urge produced by the injection is so pronounced that lacking any baby rats she will build a nest anyway. If baby mice or baby rabbits or even baby pigeons are furnished, she will do her best to mother them. Lacking any young of any kind an injected virgin rat has been known to carry her tail in her mouth repeatedly to the nest!

When the pregnancy of an animal (or of a human being) is about to terminate, nature provides through the agency of the pituitary gland the hormone necessary to induce lactation, and to promote mother love. It would not be feasible to produce by inbreeding a strain of experimental animals lacking this hormone because the young could not be taken care of or fed. It seems very probable in the light of experience with animals as well as with human beings, that individual women vary greatly in their ability to produce this hormone and that this is responsible in part not only for their differing abilities to nurse babies but also for differences in their attitudes toward babies. It is a common observation that some girls become "natural mothers" while others appear to perform their duties, if at all, only because of social pressure.

An interesting parallel exists in connection with barnyard fowls. Hens vary greatly in their tendency to become broody; some repeatedly want to "set" and will perform on a white door knob if nothing else is available. Repeated shock treatments such as dousing them with water may get the notion out of their heads, but in a short time they become broody again. In the days when baby chicks were brought up by hens it was desirable to have a few broody hens in a flock because they were generally good mothers and really looked after their flocks. The other hens (not the broody kind) seldom set, and even when they do they sometimes get tired of the job and leave the nest before hatching day.

In these days of incubators and large-scale poultry and egg production, the presence of broody hens in a flock is undesirable. It has been possible by inbreeding to rid henhood of its broodiness, to modify the inheritance of hens so that they lay, lay, lay, the year round, and never want to set. Through the use of incubators and brooders the stock can still be maintained.

Since we are discussing one aspect of biological variability in hens, let us consider another way in which it is manifest. When, for example, ten hens are placed together within an enclosure, they develop, as is well known, a hierarchy or "peck order." Number one hen can peck any other hen in the flock; number two hen can peck anyone except number one; number three can peck anyone except two and one, and so on. While these peck orders are not always perfectly rigid and may be modified somewhat when the character of the environment is changed, the fact remains that some hens are dominant creatures by nature and others are relatively submissive. That the internal production of hormones by these different hens varies, and that this variation is responsible, to a degree at least, for their varying dominance, is strongly indicated by extensive recent studies by Allee. Hens artificially injected with testosterone propionate (a sex hormone) were found to have their dominance, as measured by more than one method, greatly enhanced. A number ten hen in a flock can be transformed into hen number one!

From the standpoint of biology it appears entirely reasonable to suppose that dominating tendencies in human beings, which are often very difficult to train into people or to train out, are determined in part by innate differences in their endocrine systems.

The pituitary gland, along with its other activities, has a great deal to do with sex. The sex glands and the adrenal cortices are also involved in the complicated picture. The importance of sex in human life can hardly be exaggerated (in spite of the desire of many to do so). Even if we limit our consideration to sex crimes, we have a problem of real importance.

The strongest possible evidence for biological variability of great magnitude is to be found in Kinsey's famous study of sex behavior. Critics can object to his sampling methods and some of his conclusions, but they cannot escape, unless they deliberately close their eyes, the tremendous variability depicted. According to one important measure, normal men—those who had been able to pass for normal—varied in their sex appetites by as much as forty thousand fold. If "abnormals" were included how great would the variation be?

There can be no doubt that the sex behavior of men is subject to all sorts of environmental influences, but to one who is familiar with biological variability, there can also be no doubt that the inherited glandular system, including pituitaries, sex glands, and adrenal cortices, which is distinctive for each individual, has a great deal to do with sex variability. When two men brought up in the same society differ in their sex activities by ten, one hundred, one thousand, or ten thousand fold, there is bound to be something back of the variation besides what their mammas, or some naughty boy, told them.

The adrenocorticotropic hormone, ACTH, is another product of the pituitary gland, and presumably each pituitary may have different potentialities for producing this hormone. The fact that administering this hormone may have the effect of giving the treated individual an intense sense of well-being suggests, not that this hormone can be used routinely as a cure for the "blues," but that internal hormonal differences may have much to do with people's dispositions.

We have left out of our discussion much that could be written about the mechanism of inheritance. The subject has always been an intricate one; its intricacies have been greatly increased in recent years by the infusion of a substantial amount of biochemistry—a subject with which most people are not at all conversant. In the light of modern knowledge many of the conclusions we have drawn with respect to inheritance are absolutely inescapable. We now know a great deal about how inheritance works and how it is not only possible but certain that every human being possesses by inheritance an exceedingly complex mosaic, composed of thousands of items, which is distinctive for him alone.

Biology would seem vastly simpler and easier if variability did not exist. Human life and human planning would seem vastly less complicated if variability were absent. But actually variability is at the very basis of human life and of all life. The concept of evolution as we have it today is one in which variation is absolutely indispensable. Without genetic variability evolution could not possibly have happened, and in line with currently accepted thought, biology itself would not exist!

Biology, with variability as its cornerstone, confers on every human individual a unique set of attributes which gives him a dignity which he could not otherwise possess. Every newborn baby is an unknown quantity so far as potentialities are concerned because there are many thousands of unknown interrelated genes and gene patterns which contribute to his make-up. As a result of nature and nurture the newborn infant may become one of the greatest men or women ever to have lived. In every case he or she has the making of a distinctive individual. In some cases the distinctiveness will be far more prominent and obvious than in others. Failure to achieve success in one type of activity need not destroy morale. We will be healthier mentally if we recognize that each of us has his natural limitations. Healthy striving can be fostered by the knowledge that our distinctive potentialities are never exhausted.

One answer to Theophrastus' question is now obvious. Contributing to the make-up of every Greek was not only the climate and the education but also the genetic make-up of each distinctive member of his society. Why are people different? What they are fed physically and intellectually is only a part of the answer. We must not lose sight of inborn differences. If we do, we will limp along with half-truth. We have no assurance that half-truth will make us free.

In our modern age we make extensive practical application of the science of genetics in the growing of cattle, horses, dogs, corn, wheat, cotton, and, even of late, forest trees. In all these areas *important* characteristics are inherited. Even though we may wish to throw completely out of consideration all thought of tampering with human breeding, surely we need not blindfold ourselves to the most fundamental biological facts of human development and thus deliberately make a mess of our interpretations of life and of human nature.

III

Accounting for Tastes

THE FACT THAT PEOPLE unaccountably have diverse tastes has evidently been an enigma since ancient times. Horace in 35 B.C. said, "For so many thousand heads, as many thousand tastes." Another old Latin proverb says, "There is no disputing about tastes," which is, I suppose, equivalent to saying that no one could argue about tastes because they appeared to be completely capricious and unreasonable.

The difficulty men found in trying to understand tastes is reflected in the 400-year-old proverb (which has many slight variations), "Every man to his own taste, as the Irishman said when he kissed the cow." Another saying, "There is no accounting for tastes," is a less picturesque version expressing the same sense of futility; ascribed to John Galt, it has been used by Dickens, G. B. Shaw, and others.

If we accept the idea that people are uniform at birth, differences in taste remain wholly unexplained and unexplainable. Of course, we can fall back upon the familiar saw, "it's just a habit," but this is no explanation, because no clue is given as to how the habit originated or why, or exactly what habit is, anyway.

The simple fact that one child in a family consistently eats in his food several times as much salt as another is a case in point. It would seem farfetched, indeed, to try to explain this difference on the basis that of the two individuals eating at the same table, one would gradually "get into the habit" of eating more and more salt, while the other would gradually eat less and less. There must be some basic reason for the difference in "habits."

In this particular case we know something about the mechanisms involved, and on the basis of biological variability the enigma easily resolves itself. Salt loss from the body and the reverse—salt retention—are immediately under the control of the adrenal cortex and the hormones it produces. If one's adrenal cortex is abundantly active, the salt loss from the body is minimum; the tissues and body fluids maintain a satisfactory level of salt content and small amounts of salt daily suffice to replenish the inevitable small losses. If one's adrenal cortex is less effective in its production of hormones, salt losses increase, body fluids become somewhat depleted, and as a result of this depletion an increased appetite for salt is produced.

As made clear in the preceding chapter, people's adrenal cortices are not all the same size or of the same efficiency; neither are tasting apparatuses all the same. By inheritance we differ in these respects just as we do in the size of our noses or in the color of our eyes. For this reason some people may, from birth, have a tendency to eat less salt, and others more, and both groups may be continuously well. Since changes in one's adrenal glands and in one's tasting machinery may take place as the result of various influences, including age, the existence of inherited differences does not mean that one's appetite for salt remains unchangeable throughout life or that nothing can ever be done to alter it.

It is said that the salt consumption of individuals may vary from 2 to 30 grams per day. How important this variation is or whether high salt consumption, for example, is indicative of something else that is important, is not known. Biological variability in human beings needs vastly more study.

The relationship between adrenal glands and appetite for salt has been dramatically demonstrated using rats as experimental animals. When their adrenal cortices are damaged in various ways, their appetite for salt becomes avid and they are able to taste salt in solutions twenty times as dilute as otherwise. Administration of the cortical hormones to such rats allows salt retention, diminishes their desire for salt and abolishes their ability to taste salt in extremely dilute solutions.

Partly because there are many factors involved in one's ability to taste any particular substance as well as in one's liking for it, studies of this sort have not been favorites among research workers. There has been a tendency to admit that "there is no accounting for tastes" and let the matter rest. This neglect makes more believable the fact that the writer has been credited in a recent scientific paper, probably with far too great generosity, with being the first to report that "some substances may taste differently to different people."

The observation came about in 1925 in this way. We had submitted to us in the laboratory for identification a white crystalline substance which from various tests appeared to be a muscle constituent, creatine. But creatine was described in the chemical literature as "a bitter, biting substance," and the material submitted was perfectly tasteless—just like chalk—both to me and to my assistant. Eventually after conclusive tests, we decided that the substance, taste or no taste, *had to be* creatine, and we began submitting it to different individuals to taste. The fifth person to whom it was submitted pronounced it "bitter."

The hereditary basis for the ability to taste creatine has not been investigated, but the ability to taste another chemical, phenylthiourea, has been studied extensively from this standpoint, and has been found to be a Mendelian recessive trait.

The differences in people's ability to taste this chemical, also called phenylthiocarbamide (PTC), was discovered accidentally by Arthur L. Fox at Northwestern University. It was noted initially that one laboratory worker found the substance intensely bitter while another found it quite tasteless. This naturally led to an argument and the submission of the chemical to others for tasting. The majority found it bitter, but a substantial minority found it to be completely lacking in taste.

Subsequently A. F. Blakeslee, who was responsible for much of the genetic study, reported the submission of the substance to 6,377 people. Of these, 65.4 per cent said it was *bitter*, 21.3 per cent pronounced it *tasteless*, 5.4 per cent said it was *sour*, 4.8 per cent said *salty*, 2.1 per cent said *sweet*, and the other 1.9 per cent thought it tasted like miscellaneous fruits and vegetables—rhubarb, lemons, cranberries, etc.

Of course, the matter of people's tastes for this particular substance is interesting only because it illustrates how widely tastes can vary. From reading the percentages one might readily infer that for most people the chemical is either bitter or tasteless. One should consider, however, that if the sampling is adequate for the whole United States, there are about twenty million people for whom it would be neither tasteless nor bitter and over three million to whom it would taste sweet.

Subsequently Dr. Fox, who is now Director of Research for Colgate-Palmolive-Peet Company, informed me in private correspondence that he has noted a second chemical, sodium benzoate, which tastes radically different to different people. Some say it is salty, others find it sweet, sour, bitter, or tasteless. He has not had an opportunity to investigate the matter in a thoroughgoing fashion, but he has collected evidence to show that the people for whom both sodium benzoate and PTC are bitter have many food dislikes as compared, for example, with those to whom PTC is tasteless and sodium benzoate sweet. In the same study he has found that about 10 per cent of the population do not dislike epsom salts; "incredible, but true"!

Another substance which has been found to taste quite differently to different people is a naturally occurring sugar mannose (the name derived from manna). It is tasteless to about 15 per cent of those tested, sweet to about 20 per cent, bitter to about 10 per cent, but to the other 55 per cent it is both bitter and sweet in succession; most of these 55 per cent taste the sweet first and then the bitter, but some taste bitter first and then the sweet.

Actually the number of known compounds which would if investigated elicit markedly different taste responses in different people probably runs into the thousands. No systematic or comprehensive investigations have ever been made. In our laboratory a preliminary study of "taste thresholds" (the minimum concentration which an individual can taste in solution) for common well-known substances like sugar, sodium chloride, potassium chloride, and hydrochloric acid revealed that one hundred-fold differences are common. This means that if the proper concentration is chosen, solutions will have a taste for some people but not for others. Children were found in a Johns Hopkins University study who actually could not taste a 20 per cent sugar syrup!

The study of "taste" sensations is complicated in many ways. One of my scientific acquaintances started to embark on the study of tastes as they are related to chemical structure. He found it frequently possible to predict in advance that a particular compound would taste either sweet or bitter, but he could not foretell which. Whether he ran into differences in the taste responses of individual people, in addition to the other complications, I do not know. At any rate he gave up the study.

A complicating factor in studies of taste is that many of the sensations which we commonly ascribe to taste are actually sensations of smell. Another complication is the wide variation between individuals with respect to how things taste and how much it takes to elicit the sensation. A third is illustrated by the fact that the sense of smell (often confused with taste) varies in the same individual from hour to hour. Using coffee flavor as the material for testing, it has been reported that there is a good correlation between how hungry a person is and how acute his sense of smell is. Just before lunch, for example, his ability to smell coffee aroma is vastly superior to his ability after lunch, whether or not his lunch included coffee. Therefore, in comparing two individuals in this respect, one must test them when they are equally hungry.

The fact that extensive investigation has showed taste sensitivity for phenylthiocarbamide is inherited as a Mendelian trait, is strong presumptive evidence that other taste sensitivities are inherited also. Especially is this presumption strong because there has been nothing to prove that taste sensitivity has nongenetic origin. There are many additional findings in the general field of biochemical genetics which make the idea of genetic variability of taste thresholds entirely reasonable and practically inescapable.

The appetite for salt is not the only one related to the functioning of an endocrine gland; the appetite for calcium (lime) is determined largely by the activity of the parathyroid glands. If these glands are highly active the calcium content of the blood is high and the appetite for calcium is low. If the parathyroids are weak in their action, the calcium level in the blood falls, and the appetite for this element increases. Furthermore, because calcium and phosphates oppose each other, increased appetite for calcium is accompanied by a decreased appetite for phosphate, and decreased calcium appetite is accompanied by an increased demand for phosphate. How important these appetites are in helping us get the food we need, or how significant they may be for life, is not known but certainly ought to be known.

Special appetites for a few other food elements, including certain vitamins, have been demonstrated to exist and to have physiological bases as do the appetites for salt and calcium. If an experimental animal is deprived of thiamin (Vitamin B_1) so that the bodily supply becomes very low, it is able to detect thiamin in food and becomes ravenously hungry for anything that contains it.

It would be fortunate, in one sense, if we had special appetites for everything we need in our food and were able to depend completely on these appetites for guidance. Indeed, experiments with young children have shown that when they are allowed to choose from an assortment of wholesome natural foods, their diets appear to be satisfactory. That children will not always choose wisely, however, if candy is one of the possible choices is well known. Pressing nutritional needs are often denied (by *some* children) for the sake of sweets. Adults may also turn away from diversified nourishing foods to consume not only candy but alcohol. This furnishes fuel only—no proteins, minerals, or vitamins. Perverted and erroneous appetites, which are no doubt conditioned by the internal chemistry of the individual involved, exist along with those that are in the long run physiologically valuable.

Striking evidence that tastes are not always reliable has been shown with experimental animals which have been made deficient in the mineral element magnesium. Such animals when given a choice actually tend to avoid magnesium-containing foods. Presumably the deficiency gives them a false sense of well-being, which they do not choose to surrender!

The fact that many taste sensitivities are inherited does not mean that they remain constant throughout life or that they are unchanged by environmental influences. As we have noted in the case of salt, our body supply—how well the cells and tissues are supplied with salt—has a marked effect on our taste for it. Neither does the inheritance of taste sensitivities mean that tastes cannot be acquired or that associations have nothing to do with their development. It would be a grave mistake to assume that hereditary effects are the only ones observable in connection with taste sensations, but the fact remains that the machinery basic to taste differences is inherited.

Those who are inclined toward the assembly-line concept tend to bolster their beliefs by exaggerating the extent to which tastes are acquired and modified by experience. It is not infrequently supposed, for example, that liking for the taste of alcoholic liquor is simply a matter of training and habit. While these factors undoubtedly enter into the problem, there is ample evidence that they by no means dominate the situation.

Richter at Johns Hopkins has tested the liking for alcohol in different concentrations on the part of a large number of people including 72 children of ages varying from 4 to 10 years. Children and adults alike were generally unable to get a definite taste below about 3 per cent concentration. Among the children and adults, there were some—six of the children—who stated that they liked the taste of alcohol up through 50 per cent concentration. The failure to note any substantial difference between adults and children indicates that without any conditioning children have their distinct preferences.

That liking the taste of alcoholic drinks is not the only factor involved in the development of alcoholic addiction is shown by the fact that an appreciable number of alcoholics indicate emphatically that they *do not like the taste of liquor.* Nevertheless, it would seem probable that, other things being equal, a child with an innate liking for alcohol would have a greater tendency toward alcoholism than one who has from the outset a dislike for the taste. We shall note later how one's nutritional needs and status have a marked bearing on his tendency toward alcoholism.

In some animal experiments, we found that training and habit had less to do with alcoholic consumption than would be supposed. Animals were forced for several weeks to drink 10 per cent alcohol by giving them access to no other source of water. At the end of this time they were given a choice between water and the alcohol solution. They had less tendency to drink alcohol after the period of enforced drinking than similar rats not subjected to enforced drinking.

The fact that drinkers of distilled liquors have so many preferences with respect to exactly how they want their drinks made, whether from scotch, bourbon, rum, gin, or with and without all sorts of extras, cannot be explained on the basis of training and experience. If people were thoroughly elastic and adaptable in their tastes, everyone within a given culture would learn to drink the same drink. Presumably much of the discrimination which people have with respect to alcoholic drinks of different kinds is based upon the functioning of their olfactory or smelling apparatus. The sense of taste enters too, however, since people differ greatly with respect to whether they like alcoholic drinks that are sweet.

Individual variations with respect to the sense of smell are just as widespread as are taste differences. I know of three individuals who have ordinary sense of smell in most respects, but are unable to smell the odor of skunk, even when it is very strong. To most people the skunk odor is most unpleasant. I know of two individuals whose reaction is different. One likes the odor. The other likes it if it is not too strong.

This latter fact is not so inscrutable when we realize that people's sensitivities to odors vary through wide limits and substances which are ill-smelling at high concentration may be pleasant when diluted. Two constituents of body excretion which ordinarily are thought of as vile smelling, indole and skatole, are used in perfumery. Musk and ambergris in concentrated form have disagreeable odors, but they are also used in perfumery. Presumably the people who like skunk odor are relatively insensitive to it, and detect it only at a level that is to them agreeable.

There are people who are anosmic, having no sense of smell, and probably some have noses that are unusually keen for many scents. One investigation of Blakeslee's, however, showed that our odor perceptions are irregular and different for different odors. Blakeslee and a fellow scientist were studying the fragrance of verbenas resulting from careful plant breeding experiments and found that they did not agree with each other in their judgments. One listed four verbenas in order 1, 2, 3, 4, in terms of their fragrance; the other found the order to be the exact opposite! When they sought to settle who was right with respect to whether verbena 1 or verbena 4 was most fragrant by submitting the two kinds to forty people, they found they were both "right." Ninety per cent of those taking part in the test noted fragrance in *one* of the two, but failed to note fragrance in both.

Odors play a greater part in some lives than in others, and probably are more influential in all our lives than we realize. Personally, I take relatively little notice of odors, particularly of people. I have a friend, however, who tells me that he is continually noticing the body odors of those who call upon him in his office. He is also able to localize the odors as coming from their armpits, something that is quite beyond my experience.

As I look back to my college days, however, I remember a young lady with whom I kept company but in whom I lost interest. In retrospect, I can remember only one thing about her that wasn't wholly agreeable; there was some slight offense to my olfactory sense. Please note that I have not said that she was ill-smelling; actually to some other individual (perhaps capable of smelling different kinds of verbenas) her natural perfume may have seemed heavenly.

It is an unfortunate fact of more than passing significance that people in general—"educated" or not—are ignorant about the diversity of tastes. This causes them to be dogmatic and certain about the validity of their own. These observations apply not only to tastes in the narrower sense in which we have been discussing them, but also to tastes in literature, music, art, etc. Henry Adams said, "Everyone carries his own inch rule of taste and amuses himself by applying it triumphantly wherever he travels." Taste differences in all their ramifications, unless they are fully recognized from youth up and accepted as a part of human nature, cause rifts between people. The only antidote is understanding. In an earlier generation Emerson said, "Men lose their tempers in defending their tastes," and again, "The only sin we never forgive in each other is difference of opinion."

Must we continue to propagate our trouble-making ignorance about the simple facts of human existence, or should we make a heroic attempt to get really acquainted? Our progress in learning how to work together will depend largely upon the answer.

IV

Signatures

IT IS A WELL-KNOWN FACT that people's handwritings are distinctive, and that the validity of all legal and business documents rests upon this fact. The question of *why* handwritings are distinctive is one that is seldom considered.

On the basis of the assembly-line theory children would presumably write the way they are taught to write, and follow the prevailing mode of writing instruction. Of course the handwriting of people is influenced by school instruction, but the fact remains that even when a group follows the same copy books, each member of the group arrives ultimately at a handwriting all his own.

The writing of a signature involves coordinated movements principally of one's hand, but actually nerves traveling to and from higher nerve centers are also involved in these movements as are the nerve centers themselves. For two signatures to be the same, not only would the hands have to be precisely the same as to dimensions and musculature, but the nerves leading to and from the hands would have to conduct all impulses at the same rate and with the same efficiency and the nerve centers would have to operate identically. Hands and fingers are never precisely the same; as is well known, even the fingerprints differ. The nerves to and from these hands would rarely conduct impulses with the same efficiency and speed in two individuals; the nerve centers are not identical. The actual number, character and distribution of nerve endings in two hands are never the same. These are anatomical features like length of fingers or fingerprints themselves, and as such are basically inherited.

A forger of signatures must have excellent coördination and when successful is able to imitate the final product sufficiently well to fool the bank teller. If the time element could be included in the signatures, as for example in the form of a slow motion picture of the signing, forgers would be wholly unsuccessful. No two hands could execute a signature using the same timing for every movement and stroke, for in order to do so they would have to be identical hands and have identical nerve connections and nerve centers.

If you merely hold your hand in front of you and point to the ceiling with your index finger, you are unconsciously writing a tiny though distinctive signature in the air whether you want to or not. The signature in this case can be detected and recorded only by special means. If the movements are magnified and recorded on a moving strip, the result is an irregular wavy line. The height of the wave varies from individual to individual, and the number of complete waves produced per second is usually from six to twenty-one. These distinctive movements (finger tremors) are thought to be due to volleys of efferent nerve impulses which are constantly being transmitted.

A different kind of signature comes to light if one learns to tap out radio messages. This kind of signature is called one's "fist," and an individual operator is quite recognizable by others who are experienced in sending and receiving messages. The fundamental reason for the existence of this kind of distinctive signature is the same as for handwriting differences. In the case of tapping out radio messages the timing is included in the signature and contributes greatly to its distinctiveness.

So far we have been talking about hand signatures, but there are many other kinds. One of the most striking and individualistic of these is the kind which is recorded from one's breathing. Everyone inhales and exhales air, but the rates, depths, and the patterns of breathing are most distinctive. It is very easy to construct an apparatus which will make a continuous record of one's breathing pattern. Because of changes in depth and frequency of breathing, pauses, sighs, swallowings, etc., the tracings may look not wholly unlike the illegible handwritten signature of an executive who accentuates the up and down movements. The chance that any two breathing signatures taken at random would show a close resemblance is very remote. Many are so highly distinctive as to be identifiable almost at a glance. Breathing signatures (spirograms), like the different types of handwritten signatures, remain essentially the same year after year. This does not mean of course that they cannot change appreciably with age or that disease may not influence them.

The reason breathing patterns are distinctive for each individual is the same as for handwriting patterns. Breathing movements may be said to originate in the "respiratory center" of the brain, and the principal stimulus causing breathing movements to take place is the carbon dioxide given off by the tissues. But the size and anatomical make-up of the entire breathing apparatus is not the same for any two individuals, and the sensitivity to carbon dioxide and the operation of the respiratory center are apparently highly distinctive. Some would say that breathing is a habit; if so, then the pattern of breathing may be a habit also, but it has its roots in the inborn anatomical and neurological make-up of the individual concerned.

Human hearts produce signatures also. These are not so easily recorded as breathing signatures, but may be followed by recording blood pressures continuously or by electrocardiograms. Tiny electrical impulses are generated by heart action, and when these are amplified and recorded they are often highly distinctive, as are blood pressure records.

Human brains put out tiny electrical impulses too (brain waves), and when these are amplified and recorded it is found that no two individuals produce the same pattern of waves—and that for each individual the pattern is consistent enough so that, in the hands of experienced observers, it can serve to identify him. Since "identical twins" give patterns which are practically identical, it seems certain that the basis for this kind of signature is largely inherited.

Another type of signature is that exhibited by one's voice. By suitable electrical devices, it is possible to project on a screen a moving picture of one's voice as it is sounding forth; such pictures show in a dramatic way that voices are often highly distinctive. Most of us know, of course, that many voices can be recognized over the telephone or radio. The reasons here are the same: anatomical differences in the voice box and associated respiratory passages, sinuses, etc., and in the nerve connections. It is interesting that voices can often be mimicked with considerable success by those who by nature and training have voice flexibility. Such individuals, however, when they are talking or singing naturally, demonstrate a voice signature which is distinctly their own.

A gross type of signature is exhibited whenever a person walks, runs, dances, or swings a golf club or a baseball bat. In these cases much can be done by training to alter the signature. People can be taught to improve their posture, walk or dance more gracefully, or play golf better. Greater changes can be brought about during youth than after maturity. All of these changes, however, are superimposed upon a fundamental base—the anatomical and neurological make-up of the individual concerned—and this must be taken into account in any training effort else the effort can be misdirected or wasted.

One's manner of driving an automobile, especially through traffic, constitutes another signature. If there is space to pass between two cars, one driver may pass very close to the right-hand car and miss the one on the left by two feet, or vice versa. This is probably related to eyedness (left or right). Another driver may go through the center of the opening and still another may judge the space too narrow for safe passage. Timing is of course exceedingly important in this kind of signature; some can judge the speed of other cars, others cannot. No two individuals passing through identical traffic conditions would follow exactly the same path nor would they arrive at various points in the same time. Just as there are some people who cannot write longhand acceptably (but who may be very able in other ways) there are individuals whose anatomical and neurological make-up is such that automobile driving in traffic is for them virtually impossible.

Quite another type of signature is observed when a careful recording of body temperature is made. Different people's "normal" temperatures vary by a degree or two, and the pattern of changes throughout the day and night appear to be distinctive. In some temperature drops very substantially at night, in others it drops less, and for some temperatures come up in the morning more sharply than for others. Information with respect to individual temperature signatures is scanty (we have exhibited more interest in the temperature of distant stars), but enough measurements have been made to indicate that real signatures are involved.

Another signature which may be related to temperature signatures involves sleep patterns. Some people are most alert late in the day and into the night; some are most alert in early morning. Some can adjust their sleeping hours from day to day (or from night to day) without inconvenience; others must follow a routine or be badly upset. Some confidently affirm that these are all matters of habit, but do not have a clue as to how the habits started or why. Actually the small amount of experimental work which has been done on this problem shows that among individuals innate differences exist with respect to the character and stability of their sleep patterns as well as to their diurnal body temperature fluctuations.

Differences in regard to sleep patterns were recognized nearly two hundred years ago by a Charles Churchill who wrote this rhyme:

> In different courses different tempers run.
> He hates the moon, I sicken at the sun.
> Wound up at twelve at noon his clock goes right
> Mine better goes, wound up at twelve at night.

Instead of becoming better acquainted with the underlying causes of such attitudes in the past two hundred years, we have throttled our curiosity by a sentimental avoidance of noting inborn differences. We have erroneously thought that attention to such differences would breed misunderstanding, instead of the reverse, and that our highest goal is to understand uniform *man*, a creature who causes no trouble because he doesn't exist.

In this chapter and the preceding one we have called attention to many items involving tasting, smelling, motor activities (both voluntary and involuntary), and electrical potential patterns, all of which are distinctive for each individual. These separate items are often highly individual, not only because they are built upon distinctive individual anatomical and neurological bases, but also because of the distinctive environmental influences which come into each life.

The sum total of all of these items, as they relate to a particular individual, constitute a distinctive *pattern,* which in a sense is a signature for that individual. It is much broader than the signatures we have just discussed, because it encompasses many separate signatures. In the chapter which follows we will note that there are distinctive signatures yet to be discussed; in fact, one's whole manner of thinking constitutes a highly important signature.

V

Humanly Thinking

WHAT IS THE DIFFERENCE between the brain of a newborn infant and the brain of a newborn rat? Both must be regarded as substantially blank because up to the time of birth the brains in both cases are uninitiated and on the way to development; in neither case has the organism been in a position to receive any very meaningful sense impressions, nor has it learned how to interpret them.

But there are blanks and blanks. The blank brain of the child is capable as time goes on of accepting, digesting (perceiving), and acting upon a multitude of impressions that the brain of the rat is quite unable to handle. The brain of the child becomes the thinking apparatus of an intellectual giant, comparatively speaking, while the brain of the rat becomes at maturity simply the brain of a mature rat.

Does it not seem obvious and unquestionable that there is a difference in inheritance here? Does not the child develop *human* intelligence because it has *human* ancestors, and does not the rat have *rat* intelligence because of its *rat* ancestry? It seems to work that way in the great majority of cases!

Now we come to the question which is related to our central problem. Are the brains of all newborn babies equal not only in their blankness but in their potentialities for developing into thinking apparatuses? According to the assembly-line idea, normal babies' brains are thought of not only as equally blank but as the same kinds of blanks, with the capability of developing into a thinking apparatus of essentially the same quality. We have already pointed out how supporters of this idea may be inclined to hedge a little and admit that *slight* differences may exist. We are interested here, however, in a substantial question: Are the differences *important* or are they not? They cannot be both important and unimportant. Let us, therefore, consider various possibilities that arise in connection with the problem.

One idea rather widely held is that normal babies and children vary slightly in intelligence, but that even this is not fixed—that is, supposedly a limited supply of intelligence can be somewhat augmented by training and education. According to this idea, manifestation of intelligence is a function of age; at zero age measurable intelligence is lacking, but at 1, 2, 3, 4, 5, 6, etc., years of age it mounts up. If an individual child at six years of age exhibits the intelligence of an average six-year-old (whatever that may mean), he is said to be of "normal" or "average" intelligence. It is as though every child had intelligence corresponding to a lump of dough which swells at a certain rate during the years of development. If the rate of swelling is retarded, it is assumed that better educational methods will cause it to swell faster. At any given time the size of one's lump of dough can be determined, measured and evaluated in terms of that possessed by the "average" child of the corresponding age. There are according to this conception only three kinds of children—"retarded," "average," and "accelerated." If a child's quota of intelligence never reaches a respectable level, it is said to be retarded because educational and other developmental factors have been faulty and have caused the retardation.

From the biological viewpoint it may be supposed that the "thinking machinery" of each individual in all its microscopic details and ramifications is inherited and that just as ridges on the fingers (fingerprints) are distinctive for each individual, the wrinkles and structural features of the brain are likewise distinctive.

It may also be assumed, from the biological point of view, that every cell and structure in the brain has its function and that distinctiveness in function accompanies distinctiveness in structure. Therefore, we might accept on this basis that every newborn baby's brain taken as a whole would be a different kind of blank and that finding out the characteristics of this blank would be essential for the education and liberation of the individual possessing it. Each brain would require development, but each would be distinctive in the facility with which it could assimilate and deal with different types of thought material. Let us see if there is independent evidence to support this view.

As a first approach, what does common observation tell us? Do we find in the development of children that they assimilate different types of material with equal ease, and that when placed in the same environment they become interested in the same things, and to the same degree? It is my observation that childless adults or those who deal with children *en masse* and have had no prolonged and intimate contact with a few individual children, are much more prone to think and talk in terms of "*the* child" (a generalized creature) than are those who have reared several children in their own homes. I have never yet found a parent of several children who is inclined to deny that each has a characteristic mental make-up and temperament.

It could happen in some families of not too large size that the children, on the basis of biological inheritance, would all appear to have similar capabilities and to develop similar interests, but this seems to be the exception rather than the rule. Even in the exceptional case the appearance of similarity may be superficial. Certain it is that when we observe the general population we find tremendous divergencies which are not readily accounted for on the basis of cultural or family influences.

I had an interesting two-hour conversation some time ago with a prominent scientist which will illustrate my meaning. He holds a responsible position, world-wide in its scope, and another scientist of repute has declared concerning him: "He has one of the best minds in America."

In our conversation I mentioned the thought that different people have different *types* of minds. His retort was spontaneous and emphatic, "I *know* they do." Then he proceeded to tell me how he arrived at this conclusion.

His education on this point came after his marriage and as a direct result of it. Up to that time he had held the opinion that there were only two kinds of minds—good minds and poor minds. A "good" mind could grasp anything, including mathematical and technical principles, whereas a "poor" mind was not able to grasp technical material.

Shortly after his marriage he was shocked to discover that the woman he had taken for better or for worse was not only ignorant regarding various scientific and mathematical matters but was alarmingly uninterested and quite incapable of grasping them! This he found out when, as a follow-up of the honeymoon, he tried to teach her. He was appalled and stunned by his discovery. He wondered about his marriage and whether he had made a terrible mistake. Fortunately he took time to consider and explore the situation in which he found himself, and eventually he found out that his wife, while not possessing a mathematical-scientific mind, has a faculty for intuitive thinking and mental capacities in other directions which far surpass his own. "In some ways," he told me, "her mind can play rings around mine!"

This difference in mental pattern is exactly what one would expect on the basis of biological variability. Minds should differ in quality and pattern; it should not be possible to weigh the value of one mind against another except with respect to single, special abilities. If we believe the scientist's evaluation, the wife had the superior mind in some respects and the husband in others. (Incidentally, the mutual recognition of this fact could not do other than promote domestic understanding and peace.)

Sometimes an exaggerated instance will demonstrate a truth which we cannot otherwise see. A professor of chemical engineering in one of the state universities tells of a young student who was, as the saying goes, head, shoulders, and belly above anyone else in the class. He had such a fine understanding and appreciation of every chemical concept that the professor marveled at him. However, George (let's call him) was an atrocious speller; he continually misspelled even simple words, much to the dismay of his teacher. Finally the professor took him aside and asked him why he didn't learn to spell. He advised him to concentrate on it and to check with the dictionary if he had any doubt. George's reply was, "I've tried it, Professor, but in order to look up words, you have to know how they start!"

George had the traditional training and education. If the uniformity doctrine holds and his mind were an average one, he would probably have learned to spell reasonably well, and chemistry would have been difficult for him. Actually with a distinctive (and unusual) mental make-up and pattern of potentialities he had great difficulty with spelling, and chemistry was as easy as falling off a log.

A historical case of a highly unusual mental pattern is that of a young man named Gottfried Mind, who was born in Switzerland in 1768. He was like too many unfortunate children in that he was unable to learn his lessons. There was something wrong with his thinking apparatus and he had a difficult time learning how to talk. He was never able, even when he became adult, to read and write, nor could he as an adult tell what the various coins were for. He couldn't make change. How does it happen then that his name and the date of his birth are known nearly two hundred years afterward? His mind lacked a number of potentialities, but there was one area in which it responded and things made sense. This was in the field of art. In art he was a superior individual. He delighted in making drawings and water color sketches particularly of animals, cats, deer, rabbits, bears, and occasionally of groups of children! His pictures of cats were so good that he was called "The Cat's Raphael." One of his pictures of a cat and kittens was purchased by King George IV, and he became known all over Europe!

It is interesting to note the fact that Gottfried Mind was probably suffering from thyroid deficiency and that this may have been the cause of his unusual mental deficiencies. This is not to say, however, that treatment for this condition would have resulted in a patternless mind in which all mental endowments would have been at a dead level. It is idle to speculate, but with all his faculties greatly augmented, it is possible that he would have developed into a really great artist.

It is not unheard of for people to have minds which are in a sense quite the opposite of that possessed by this classic case. They are able to talk fluently, to read and write, and may be extremely proficient in making (and keeping) change, but as for drawing and painting aptitude they are a total loss—quite as incompetent as Gottfried Mind was, but in a different area.

The number of mind patterns that have actually been observed is very large. A more recent case of a very unusual pattern is that of a man whose case was reported when he was 23 years old. He never learned to talk, much less to read and write. In fact, he couldn't even understand language well enough to point correctly to his nose or ears when requested to do so. But his potentialities for learning were not all deficient, and there was one area where his mind clicked. Numbers made sense to him. In fact, they made such good sense and were so well understood that he was able later to perform phenomenal stunts with them. While ordinary writing made no sense to him (possibly no more than it would to a dog or elephant), the symbols for numbers registered, and as a small youngster he began scribbling them at every opportunity.

His writing of numbers was not imitative, either; he knew what they meant. If for example a series 2, 4, 8, 16 was started he was able to continue it indefinitely. The idea of square roots was conveyed to him merely by writing down numbers like 9 and 3 side by side, and when 625, 729, and 900 were then written he wrote the square roots opposite them. If two numbers, each with several digits, were written down one below the other he would multiply them together mentally and write down only the answer.

Another type of mind pattern was exhibited by José Capablanca. While his prowess in other directions was not outstanding, his aptitude for the game of chess was. On a day when he was five years old he was watching his father and a crony play chess, as he had done often before; he noted an error his father had made and called his attention to it after the game. His father, who was a chess enthusiast but not a champion, was surprised that the youngster knew anything about it. José assured him, however, that he could play. The father then allowed his son to play a game to demonstrate, and the five-year-old easily beat his father. He was taken to the Havana Chess Club, where he played with the experts. The best players could beat him, but by no means easily. At the age of twelve, he won the championship of Cuba. Up to this time, he had never had a lesson in chess and had read only one book on chess—one dealing with endings. His opponent, Corzo, was a specialist on chess openings, about which young Capablanca knew little. In the final contest of the tournament, between Corzo and Capablanca, the one first to win four games was to be declared champion; at the end of two games it looked bad for the youngster because he had lost both. But his opponent had unwittingly taught him in these two games a vast deal about chess openings. The next five games were draws and the next four were won by the twelve-year-old. Later in his career Capablanca in Cleveland played 103 chess games simultaneously, winning all but one, which was a draw. He played rapidly, rarely taking more than a minute to make a move, and when the Cleveland demonstration was over he complained only that his *feet* were tired. For seven hours he had been going from table to table. He claimed not to have exerted himself mentally. Can anyone seriously doubt that at birth Capablanca had a distinctive endowment which made chess easy to learn?

Still another mental pattern which shows great contrast (strength and weakness side by side) was exhibited by a boy in Indiana who was studied briefly at the University of Indiana. His ability in most school work was less than mediocre (in fact, he was classed as a high-grade moron), but there was one thing about his thinking machinery that worked remarkably well. It had to do with his memory, particularly for numbers.

He could watch a freight train go by at a railroad crossing and note the numbers on all the cars (some of the numbers running into five and six digits); after the train had passed, he could reel off from memory the numbers of every car in order.

Many isolated examples of extraordinary memory ability could be cited; a boy who memorized the numbers in an entire telephone book; a Hindu girl that my mother used to tell about who knew the entire New Testament verbatim; another boy who had a complete mental file of the vital statistics of the people in his community. Some of these people were lame in other respects, but not always. In any case their memories were extremely effective.

Many cases are known, both of children who are otherwise reasonably well equipped and of those who are not, in which the individuals possess unusual musical ability. A case of striking contrast in mental pattern is that of a blind "imbecile" girl reported from an institution in Vineland, New Jersey. In spite of her blindness and other deficiencies, her mental abilities in the field of music were such that she could play difficult works on the piano after hearing them only once. On one occasion a visiting musician tested her by playing for her an unpublished composition of his own. She asked to hear it a second time, then sat down at the piano and played it perfectly.

There are a good many people whose mind patterns do not show, on cursory examination, strong contrasts. Their abilities in different directions (especially those called upon in school work) are approximately at the same level. They seem able to learn spelling, arithmetic, science, languages, and music with nearly equal facility. Such individuals (who if all avenues were explored would not be patternless) often get positions of educational influence and are difficult to convince as to the importance of mental patterns. A strong tendency to judge on the basis of one's self makes such individuals adhere to the lump of dough theory, incidentally admitting of course that they possess a sizeable lump themselves.

Many of the individuals who have made a great impression on the world have, however, showed highly contrasting patterns. Let us consider, for example, the case of a man whose mathematical ability and physical insights have astounded the world—Albert Einstein.

It should not dim the brilliance of his genius to point out that his supermentality does not extend in all directions. In other words, he has a mental *pattern,* with contrasts, and this exhibited itself at an early age. In certain respects he was not a precocious child—far from it. He was so slow in learning to talk that his parents feared that he was deficient—which he actually was *in this respect.* Even at nine years of age he was halting and slow of speech. He was unable to learn by rote (he couldn't have begun to do what the Indiana "moron" could do) and was deficient in languages, geography, and history, all of which were predominantly memory work.

But Einstein was "precocious" in his own way. When he was four years old, his father gave him a small magnetic compass, thinking it would amuse him. Instead, it impressed him profoundly and intrigued his interest. Even at this early age his deep-seated profundity, in asking why, was showing itself. Along lines in which his aptitude lay, Einstein forged ahead. At fourteen he had gone a long way toward the mastery of algebra, analytic geometry, differential and integral calculus, working largely by himself.

Someone has suggested that Einstein has the greatest intellect of any man who ever lived. Such a statement is based upon the lump of dough conception of intelligence. Certainly one could say that along mathematical and physical lines his mind appears to be at the top. As a linguist, however, he would not rate higher than mediocre, as is attested by his early record and by the fact that several of his books were written in

German and translated by others into English. If he had the endowments of an able linguist, he would have exhibited them in his youth; he would have learned to speak his native tongue earlier than he did; he would have learned English earlier and used it; his literary ability as a writer would be greater than it is.

Unusual mechanical ability, outstanding ability in designing and building, marked aptitude in wood carving or in sculpture, have all been found in individuals who had no outstanding aptitude along other lines. Contrasting mental patterns are the rule, not the exception; their importance can best be appreciated by one who has himself a contrasting pattern.

Along some lines my own mind seems to work reasonably well, but there is one area, at least, that is decidedly weak. I have now, and have had all my life, great difficulty in memorizing material which makes no appeal either to my reason or to my emotions. Dates in history, proper names which carry no meaning, formulas of organic compounds with which I haven't worked, foreign vocabularies, telephone numbers—all these are very difficult for me, even though it would be greatly to my advantage if the weakness were not there. When I say that my aptitudes along this line are severely limited, I do not mean to infer that I am wholly unable to memorize material of this sort; it is merely that many other people I know do it by comparison with the greatest ease.

Another different but not wholly unrelated observation of undoubted validity, even when considered by itself, places the assembly-line adherent in a most difficult position. If we should grant that normal newborn babies are essentially alike in their capabilities, what can be said of the mentally deficient? Are they alike too, only *different?* Is inheritance of no importance here? If not, why are the offspring of first cousins and of incestuous unions more often the victims? In such cases, of course, "ganging up" of recessive characteristics is possible. Any concept of human nature which cannot include the mentally deficient is certainly fallacious, especially so because of the great difficulty which persists in all attempts to draw a sharp line between the "normal" and the "abnormal."

Before we pass on the question of what the more formal psychological evidence tells us about the uniformity or nonuniformity of newborn infants, let us make clearer how ideas of inheritance fit in with the general biological view and with the various observations which we have just discussed.

Let us consider, for example, a time-honored question. Is musical ability inherited? This question itself conveys an erroneous idea which must be uprooted before the problem can be considered intelligently. The formulation of this question is based upon the assumption that musical ability is like a bump on the lump of dough; it is *one* thing; you either have more of it or less. Actually, however, there are various factors which enter into the make-up of a musician.

Let us suppose that a prospective mother is anxious above all things that her offspring be a musician of the highest type, and further that she can by calling on the gods get him whatever endowments he might need. What should she ask for?

According to Seashore's exhaustive studies, there are at least six different *measurable* items that enter into musical ability. One is ability to discriminate between different pitches, one is ability to distinguish between different intensities of tones, another involves timing and rhythm, another involves being able to tell when tones blend or are in discord, the fifth involves memories of tones, and the sixth, which is not so easy to measure, is imagery. In addition to all these, and probably of paramount importance, is the emotional element, the ability which we acknowledge when we say someone "puts his soul" into a musical performance.

These are, of course, not all the things that the prospective mother might ask for. Lengthy fingers would help a prospective pianist and a good neuromuscular set-up would be indispensable. The neuroanatomy of the larynx and the whole breathing apparatus would be important for a singer, and general good looks would help to insure success.

No musician living or dead has had all these abilities to the highest degree. They have *patterns* of abilities with contrasts. Seashore cites examples of musicians who have done very well in spite of rather severe weaknesses of a specific nature.

Now, let us look again into the question of inheritance. According to the biological concept *each of the elements which enters into the make-up of a potential musician is inherited.* Because of the numerous factors involved and the fact that traits appear in individuals which do not appear in their parents (but do appear in earlier forebears), the inheritance of musical abilities is extremely complicated and the results largely unpredictable. For example, a father and mother could each be sufficiently lacking in some essentials so that neither would be regarded as having "musical ability." Yet the offspring of this union, even though traits of earlier forebears did not appear, might, by combining the qualities of the two parents, have the potentialities for becoming a great musician.

Actually, of course, the chance of a great musician arising is much better if the father and mother are both good musicians—not only from the hereditary standpoint, but from the standpoint of training.

The broader question, "Is intelligence inherited?" must be handled in the same way. If intelligence were like a lump of dough, then the solution of the problem would be relatively easy: Measure the lumps of dough of children and their forebears and see if there is a mathematical correlation. But the potentialities for mental development contain numerous factors—no one knows yet how many—and the best we can say is that from the biological standpoint *every element which enters into intellectual potentiality is inherited.*

It is worthy of note here that when one inherits a pattern of intellectual potentialities, the individual elements in the pattern do not necessarily remain as discrete entities. They may combine and interact in such a way as to yield something unique. A distinctive pattern may thus be distinctive both because of the unique assortment of elements present and also because of what has resulted from their interaction.

Next, let us consider what light psychological research can throw on this very important problem. The one investigator who is farthest advanced in this area (most psychologists are interested in other things) is L. L. Thurstone, recently of the University of Chicago. On the basis of his productivity, his position, and the honors that have come to him, he must be regarded as one of the top-notch psychologists of this country and of the world.

He has utilized a mathematical scheme called "factor analysis" by which it is possible to determine whether mental ability is unitary or multiple in nature. The technique involves giving to a large group of "guinea pigs" a large number of different kinds of tests (or tests containing a number of different elements). By mathematical analysis of the results it is possible to ascertain whether the different elements in the tests correlate with each other in the different individuals. If an individual is superior in one area in which he is tested, will he be superior in other areas too? Do the various signs of mental ability always remain clustered together in certain individuals or are they found to be separable?

The answer to this question found by strictly objective scientific methods is unequivocal. Just as one might anticipate on the basis of the biological evidence, excellent mental abilities of various types are found dissociated from each other; they are by no means always clustered together. This is another way of saying that patterns of mental abilities exist and the lump of dough idea is untenable.

On the basis of his study Thurstone finds that several "primary mental abilities" exist. Among the most clear-cut of these are: arithmetical facility, ability to memorize by rote, spatial imagery, and word familiarity. Whether each of these is strictly an indivisible unit may be questioned, and no one knows how long the list of primary mental abilities will be when complete. The essential idea that patterns exist and that the above list constitutes, at least as a good first approximation, some of the items in the pattern, can hardly be doubted.

The conspicuous presence, or absence, of some of these primary abilities may be noted in the cases which have already been mentioned. The boy who could not read, write, or carry on a conversation nevertheless had extraordinary arithmetical facility. The boy who could remember all the numbers on the freight cars was poor in arithmetic and other school subjects, but his ability to memorize by rote was astounding. Capablanca must have had along with other abilities (probably including the ability to memorize by rote), outstanding spatial imagery. He would have to perceive and remember spatial relations on the chess board, which most people could not grasp at all. The chemistry student, George, evidently had a substantial assortment of excellent mental abilities, otherwise he could not have understood chemistry so well, but his pattern included a weakness in the area of word familiarity, for this is exactly the ability which makes people good spellers, makes them able to build anagrams and perform other stunts with words.

Certainly one of the most significant parts of the investigation of Thurstone and his co-workers is the investigation of the mental patterns of homozygous ("identical") and other twins. Not only do mental patterns exist, but Thurstone has become convinced, as he indicated in a speech at the Centennial Celebration of the American Association for the Advancement of Science in 1948, that *the individual mental capacities are inherited.* The mental patterns of homozygous twins are so much alike, as determined by mathematical analysis, that no other explanation is possible.

On the basis of (1) common observation, (2) what appears to me to be irrefutable biological evidence, and (3) specific objective psychological findings, the conclusion appears clear although probably, to some, startling: *Every newborn baby has a distinctive and complex pattern of inborn mental capacities. Each item in this pattern is derived from his human forebears, but the pattern with its interactions is unique.*

The existence of limitations in each pattern should be recognized, since this recognition can be a face saver for all of us as well as a guard against accepting dictators and others who pretend to, but cannot, know it all. The positive aspect of the conclusion needs also to be stressed. We all have potentialities far greater than we develop, but too often they may be in directions different from our striving. It is pathetically true that many people go through life without ever finding themselves and many more fail to find themselves until the energy of youth is largely dissipated.

The importance of the conclusion as stated above would indeed be difficult to exaggerate, since it has a crucial bearing not only on education but also on every conceivable human situation whether it be social, economic, political, diplomatic, artistic, religious, or what not.

It is because of this importance that for a number of years I have been singularly interested in the possibilities residing in the field of psychology, a field that traditionally has been far removed from biochemistry but will one day be intimately intertwined with it.

However, behavioristic psychology, which is strongly environmentalistic, naturally neglects that which is inborn in each of us and for this reason cannot possibly perform the functions of an all-round psychology which takes into account all the important facts. Psychology must become aware of the biological basis of intelligence; it must abandon its optimism with respect to understanding "the human mind" and attack more directly than ever before the task of understanding people as they are.

In education this insight is sorely needed. As we shall point out in a later chapter in more detail, if education is to perform the wonders of which it is capable, it *must* work in line with the inborn capacities of the people to be educated.

Will Rogers must have had the idea of mental patterns in mind when he said, "We are all ignorant. We are just ignorant about different things." Donald Culross Peattie has commented beautifully about these words and I quote with his permission:

"Here are words to make a man smile—then bow his head a moment, and finally stand all the straighter. For they give him courage, even as they make him humble.

"They tell us how much we need one another. They show us how each of us has his place and his job to do. They level us all down, and then lift us all up, in eagerness, in hope to learn a little about the lot we don't know. Said with the easy kindness of a man at once simple and wise, they are a directive toward democracy.

"The pride of the intellectual is a Lucifer danger, which in recent past has led fine minds as far as the betrayal of their country. The know-how of the expert can be, without wider vision, no more than a blind alley. The fixed idea of the opinionated is as dangerous as a blunt instrument. And the complacency of the incurious is a kind of death in life.

"But to know how little you know, and to turn—with the friendliness of a Will Rogers—to others to learn from them is worthy of the greatest mind and possible to the least instructed.

"We must seek, across all barriers of kind and caste, of country and color, to understand those ignorant of what we know, yet wise in their own ways. Only then will we master the ultimate lesson—how to live together in peace here on earth, our common home."

VI

Humanly Wanting

WHY IS LIFE worth living? What do you like most about it or want most from it? From what do you get your most thorough satisfactions? Are you substantially like others in your wants, or do your life desires add up to a distinctive pattern?

For anyone to enumerate and give the proper weight to the various attractive items in his life is not easy, but let us make a first attempt by considering the contents of the forty-eight numbered "boxes" listed on pages 57, 58, and 59.

In order to make the task not too complicated, the number of boxes was restricted. The contents of the various boxes do not always belong together with perfect appropriateness. Almost every one of the boxes as indicated could be cut up into smaller boxes and considered separately, but in this case the number of items would be excessively large. It is not presumed that every possible satisfaction-giving item is included in the list, though it is hoped that the more important ones will be found. Detailed items relating to specific occupational activities are in general omitted.

There are inevitably cases of overlapping between the boxes, in which case the components must be separated in your own mind as well as possible. For example, in case you enjoy playing cards for money, it may be that the card playing is the primary source of enjoyment, in which case you could enjoy the game even if there were no betting. Possibly on the other hand playing cards is merely an excuse for betting, the thing that you really enjoy. Still another possibility is that you enjoy both card playing and betting and each adds enjoyment to the other. Similarly there is overlapping if a young man gets keen enjoyment out of looking at beautiful girls; it may be the sex angle that is primary and the beauty secondary. If beauty is of real importance, he will enjoy beauty in forms quite apart from women.

If you wish to be a guinea pig and play the game, it may result in a self-portrait which will be revealing. In selecting and choosing between the various boxes it will probably not be desirable to use your imagination too freely. For example, if you have never hunted at all and yet imagine that you would be crazy about lion hunting, it would hardly be in keeping with the purposes of the game to list hunting as one of your top sources of satisfaction. On the other hand anyone who has a strong creative urge, no matter how imperfectly it has been realized in the past, should be entitled to list creative work as a source of satisfaction.

The rules of the game we are about to play call for dealing with each of these separate boxes as a unit. If there is something you like very much in one of the boxes, hold on to that box. It is not supposed that you will necessarily like everything, or even most things, in any given box.

Another rule of the game is to try to think of the various items from the standpoint of an over-all view of your adult life. Do not follow merely your present mood. For example, do not rate eating food high because you happen to be hungry at the moment, or do not rate it low because you have just finished an ample meal.

Another essential rule is that you think of the items as satisfaction-giving, pleasurable, and attractive items—not as items that may be necessary for some other reason. We have not listed "breathing" as an item in any of the boxes. It is something that we all do and, if we were listing items which we would not like to be deprived of, it certainly would be near the top of the list because it is essential to life. We have presumed, however, that it is not something worth living *for* and that most people do not get any particular satisfaction or fun out of mere breathing. One phase of the eating of food may involve the same component. Do not rate eating of food at a high level because of the well-known fact that you can't live without eating. Rate it high only in relation to its satisfaction-giving or pleasure-giving value.

Another desirable rule, which may be difficult to follow strictly, is to avoid passing moral judgments on your own selections; further, do not concern yourself with how someone else might regard your selections. The boxes are listed alphabetically on the basis of some key word, in order to avoid any indication of priority of value of one box over another. Let's assume that it is perfectly all right to like any item listed, to any degree, and try to arrive at the true status of your likes and dislikes.

In making choices—this is an essential part of the game—it is suggested that you ask yourself this question: If I were traveling to an imaginary "heaven" in which my own desires would be met and had to choose, for example, between boxes 9 and 10 (not being permitted to take both), which would I take and which would I discard? In making a choice, for example, between box 8 and box 23, ask yourself: Would I willingly leave a good card game to enjoy the pleasure of eating, or would I gladly postpone a good meal in order to continue the fun of playing cards? In order to be sure that pleasure rather than necessity is the factor you are considering in connection with food, you might ask yourself these questions: Would I just as soon take my nourishment in capsule form if this were possible? Do I look forward to eating? Do I take plenty of time to prolong the pleasure of eating or do I get it over as soon as possible?

Do not be too literal in your interpretation of what is included in a particular box. If something you get enjoyment out of is fundamentally similar to a specific item listed in a given box, go ahead on the assumption that your item is also included in that box.

This game was played at my request by ten people—five men and five women; the results turned out to be extremely interesting and are given (anonymously) in detail a little later. Before paying too much attention to these results, however, it may be desirable for you to go through the selecting process just as they did. In any event you should not be influenced by the choices of someone else.

Here is how to proceed:

First, discard every box which contains items of practically negligible importance for you. There is no definite rule saying just how many

1. Aiding people personally, contributing to their health and/or welfare.

2. Alcoholic beverages: all forms of alcoholic drinks—ales, beers, wines, gins, whiskies, liqueurs, etc., in whatever form served, with meals or separately.

3. Athletic activities (participation) including all kinds of athletic games as well as swimming, dancing, skating, skiing, hiking, mountain climbing.

4. Babies: enjoying babies and small children.

5. Beauty: enjoying it as seen through the eyes; scenery, sunsets, art, etc.

6. Betting: on contests, races, elections, pin-ball machines, roulette, etc., whether for small stakes or large.

7. Buying and/or selling: bargaining, shopping, dickering.

8. Card games of all sorts.

9. Carnival: crowds, roller coaster, ferris wheel, carousel, etc.

10. Chess, checkers, and similar games.

11. Citizenship: being a good citizen, contributing to civic improvement.

12. Collecting: postage stamps or what have you.

13. Comic papers and books.

14. Constructing, planning (including house planning), making articles from metal, wood, etc., crafts, needle work, fancy work, etc.

15. Conversation: hearing and telling stories, chit chat, visiting, bull sessions, political discussions, parties, teas (leaving out the food components).

16. Correspondence: writing and receiving letters.

17. Creative work in art, music, literature, sculpture, science.

18. Dogs: enjoyment of these and other household pets.

19. Domination of others, exercising prestige, being boss.

20. Dramatic performance, exhibiting prowess.

21. Exploring: travel, seeing new places, new people.

22. Fishing: all sorts whether in streams, lakes, rivers, and oceans.

23. Food: all kinds including candies and confections.

24. Gardening: all sorts.

25. Horses: enjoyment of, horseback riding, etc.

26. Hunting of all kinds: small game, birds, large game.

27. Listening to speeches.

28. Loafing, solitude, contemplating one's navel.

29. Massage, scalp massage, shampoo.

30. Medical care: being diagnosed, treated, and nursed.

31. Membership in clubs, fraternities, lodges, service organizations, working on committees.

32. Model trains, model airplanes, model boats, etc. Being a radio ham.

33. Music of all kinds: appreciation and/or performance.

34. Nature: such activities as bird watching, studying or observing the stars, rocks, plants (including trees), and/or animals.

35. Odors: enjoyment of all kinds, natural or artificial.

36. Ownership of property (of all sorts) for the pleasure of ownership.

37. Photography: taking pictures of all kinds and enjoying them.

38. Puzzles of all kinds: crossword, etc., mechanical, mathematical.

39. Reading: all kinds, light or heavy, fiction, nonfiction, poetry, newspapers, magazines, books.

40. Religious worship: activity or contemplation directly and consciously concerned with God.

41. Riding in or driving cars, planes, boats, etc.

42. Routine activities: daily duties, regular occupation and work.

43. Self adornment: dressing up, enjoying good clothes and making good appearance, using jewelry, cosmetics.

44. Sex: including sex arousal, courting, petting, flirtation.

45. Shows of all kinds: radio, movie, television, legitimate plays, vaudeville, etc.

46. Thinking, planning, contriving, inventing.

47. Tobacco in all its forms.

48. Watching or following athletic contests, races, etc.

boxes you must discard. You may eliminate three-fourths or more, or possibly one-fourth or less. That is up to you. In order to get the most out of the game, however, consider the boxes as though they were pieces of baggage to be taken on a journey, and eliminate when you can. List on a sheet of paper the numbers you retain as significant (List 1).

Second, from the remaining boxes eliminate those which are slightly attractive but are unimportant. These are the ones which you wouldn't mind having along but you wouldn't want to go to any extra trouble to retain. The new list of retained boxes (List 2) should now be materially smaller than List 1.

Third. Indicate which of the remaining boxes are important but of *secondary* importance. These you would like to retain and would go to some trouble to retain but they could be dispensed with if the baggage restrictions were severe. Make a new and smaller list of the numbers retained (List 3).

Fourth. Imagine now that having discarded every box of secondary importance your boat is still overloaded and you have encountered heavy seas on your voyage to "heaven." As a precautionary measure you must discard one-third to one-half of the boxes you have brought along thus far. Which will you retain? Make a fresh list of the numbers (List 4).

Let us suppose now that because of some peculiarities in the customs regulations it is now necessary for you to place a value on each of the boxes in List 4, according to the following rules: Each box must be given at the minimum a rating of 4. No box can be given a rating higher than 10.

In order to make these ratings you may find it helpful to do some imaginary trading among the boxes retained in List 4. If any box in this list is equal in value to two others, it cannot have a rating of less than 8, since each one must be rated at least 4.

When you have finished with the four lists and the rating of the numbers in List 4, the scoring is easy. For each item not included in any of your lists the score is 0. Any item appearing *only* in List 1 is scored 1, those in both List 1 and List 2 are scored 2; those in Lists 1, 2, and 3 are scored 3, and those in List 4 are scored 4 or more depending upon the ratings you have already given.

Next let us turn to the results obtained from the ten anonymous individuals so that you can, if you wish, compare your results with theirs. Certainly we obtained from them no recognizable picture of that dubiously dubbed abstraction "the normal human being"; instead we got pictures of ten human beings, each surprisingly different from the others.

The five men and five women were associated with our Biochemical Institute staff (not necessarily as scientists), but we arranged it so that only one person (not myself) knew who took the test, and their individual records bear no identification whatever. It is not presumed, of course, that these ten were by any means a fair sample of the general population; the group happened to be weighted with younger people who are scientifically inclined, and everyone was married or had been married. Two sets of husbands and wives were included. All of the individuals gave evidence of being "well-adjusted" and all were regularly employed or occupied with congenial tasks. Since the group was in a sense a selected one, it might be supposed that the members would show greater similarities to each other than would members of a group taken at random from the general population.

It is not presumed that the results of the test were in any sense perfect or that the individuals had always answered in strict honesty or accordance with facts—a certain amount of wishful thinking is bound to creep in. On some items they were perhaps deluding themselves. But, in any event, they were all confronted with the same selections, and their diverse reactions (whether fanciful or not) are revealing as to their personality patterns.

We were prepared for some diversity on the basis of much of the material presented in this book as well as general observation, but the diversity of patterns turned out to be extreme—*far beyond* what we had anticipated, especially so since many of the members of the group were alike in that they had similar scientific leanings.

There was not a single item in the entire list which was not discarded as worthless by at least one of the ten. There were only two items, Carnivals and Model Trains, discarded by all of the ten. (If the group had been larger or a different assortment, these items would have received a high rating by some.) No single item, including the top scoring ones, Reading and Sex, was given a high score (4 or higher) by more than six out of the ten. One box, Correspondence, was given a very high score (8) by one person, but was scored zero by six others. Another, Medical Care, was given a high score of 4 by one individual and zero by eight others. Food was scored 8 by one, zero by another, and the others gave it intermediate scores, three of them 1. Citizenship was scored 3 by two individuals, 1 by four, and the rest gave it zero scores. Music was scored zero by two, and 10, 8, 8, and 4 by four others. Ownership of Property was scored 8 by one, zero by four, and 1 by three. Religious Worship was scored 10, 8, 8 by three, and zero by three others.

It is interesting that this particular group of individuals gave very low—nearly zero—scores to Fishing, Hunting, Horses, Collecting, and Dramatic Performance. These individual items (as well as Carnival and Model Trains which actually received zero scores) would without question be scored very high by some individuals that I know personally.

This further illustrates that the diversity which we have observed in our group of ten would be greatly magnified if the group were larger.

For our particular group the *average* scorings were in the following order:

1. Reading
2. Sex
3. Thinking
4. Babies
5. Conversation
6. Music
7. Creative Work
8. Beauty
9. Worship
10. Aiding People
11. Exploring
12. Food
13. Constructing
14. Shows
15. Alcoholic Beverages
16. Dogs
17. Watching Athletics
18. Ownership
19. Self Adornment
20. Correspondence
21. Riding
22. Athletic Participation
23. Nature
24. Citizenship
25. Cards
26. Routine Activities
27. Tobacco
28. Loafing
29. Photography
30. Betting
31. Chess, Checkers
32. Domination
33. Gardening
34. Buying, Selling
35. Collecting
36. Comics
37. Fishing
38. Medical Care
39. Massage
40. Odors
41. Puzzles
42. Dramatic Performance
43. Hunting
44. Horses
45. Listening to Speeches
46. Membership, Clubs
47. Carnival
48. Model Trains

On the basis of the scores for the forty-eight items, as given by each of the ten individuals, we prepared the graphs 1–11, using the above order to plot the items. The average of the ten (graph 11) is wholly different from any individual in the group; it might be considered as an attempt to depict the wants of the "hypothetical average man" but as such is meaningless so far as the wants of *real individuals* are con-

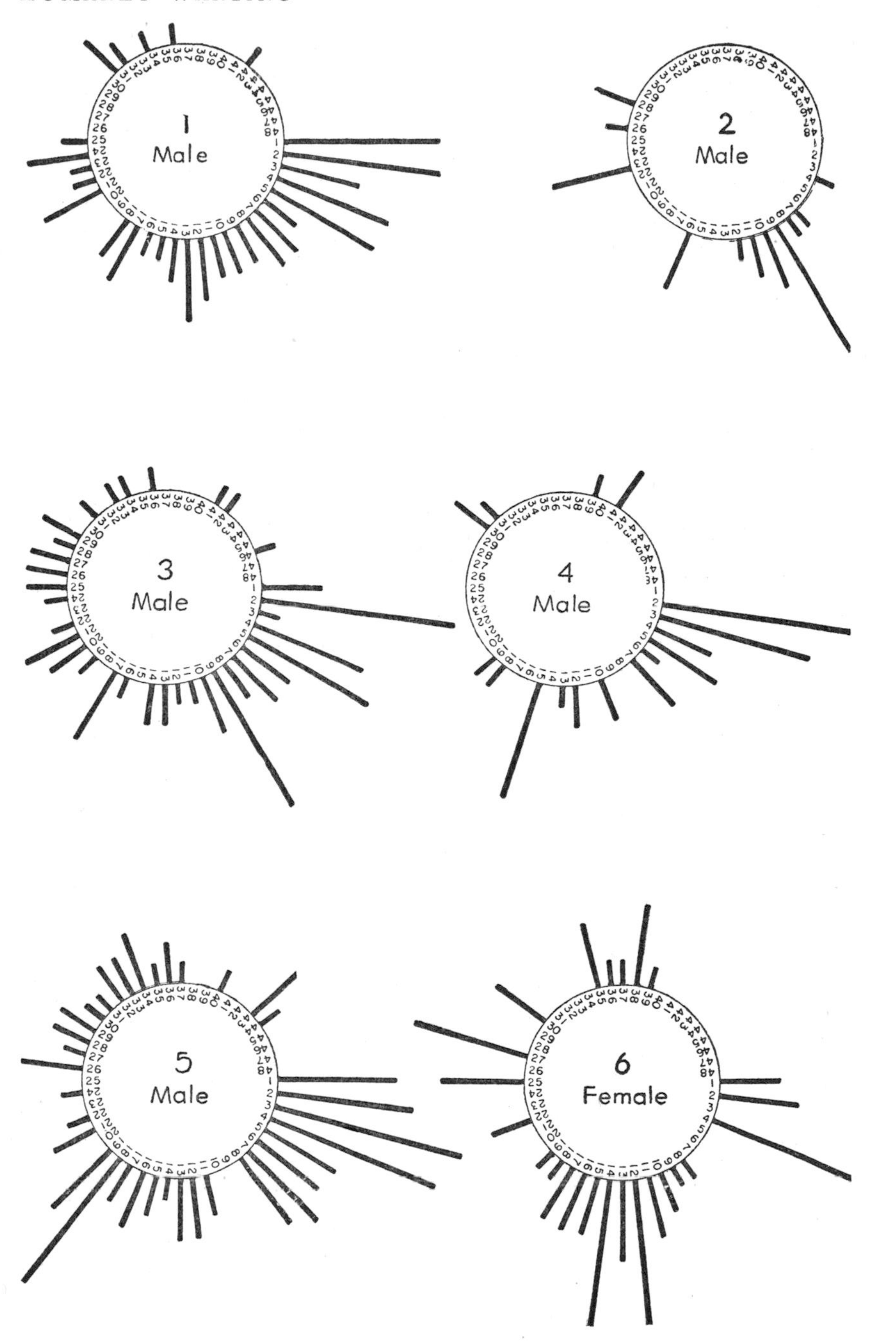
1
Male
2
Male
3
Male
4
Male
5
Male
6
Female

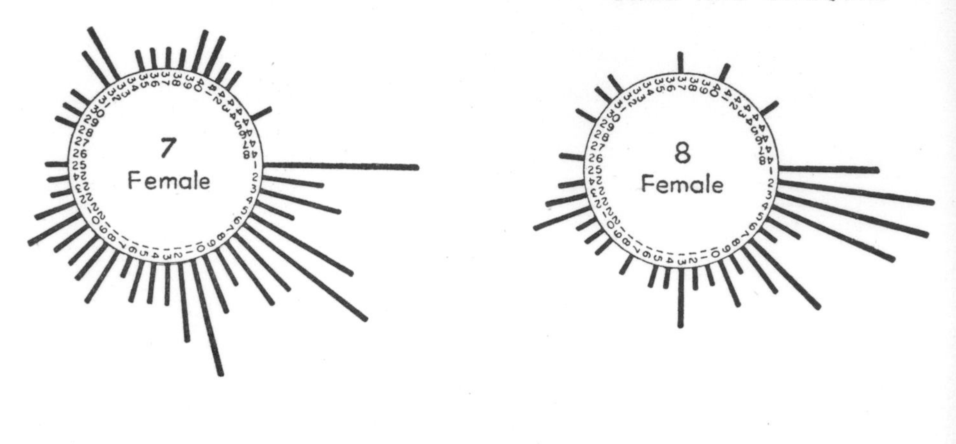
7
Female
8
Female

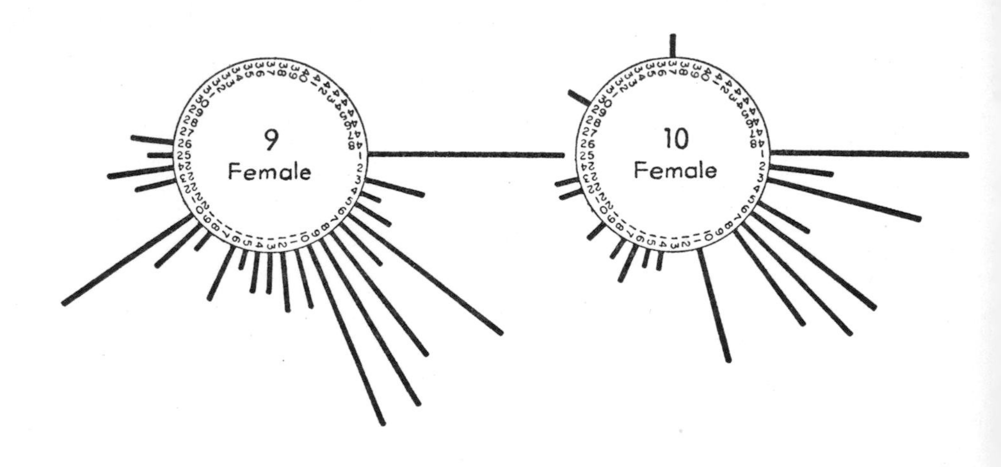
9
Female
10
Female

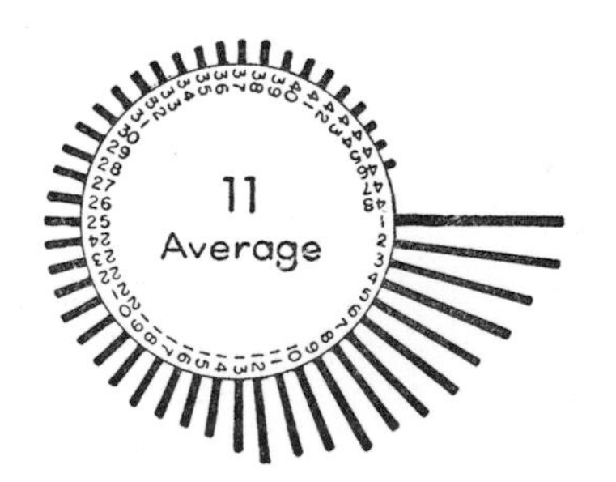
11
Average

cerned. Each individual in the group exhibited a pattern of wants characteristic of himself alone.

That the differences exhibited by these individuals do not involve unimportant details needs emphasis. The preference for chess over checkers, or Wagner over Beethoven, is not involved; instead we are concerned with broad, far-reaching human activities, which are closely bound with the significance of life itself.

If you have been an actual participant in the game we have outlined, you can now make a partial self-portrait patterned after those on pages 63 and 64. Even if you limit yourself to graphing as few as twelve items, you will find that you have a picture which is distinctive for *you*. If your picture appears to be distorted or lopsided or much unlike any others, do not be concerned. That lopsidedness is *you*, madam, or *you*, sir! It is your own particular pattern and there is no normal "*man*" with whom you can sensibly be compared.

Consideration of these "want patterns," including those of yourself and friends, leads to the question: *Why* are they so diverse? To answer this question adequately would require by itself at least a volume. The characteristic "signatures" of various people enter into the problem, as well as the differences in sensory reactions, tastes, endocrine patterns (no doubt highly important), aptitudes (art, music, etc.), and, at the intellectual level, the differences in people's mental patterns. All of these enter into making our wants what they are. Training and education no doubt enter in an important way into the development of many likes and dislikes. Living in a musical home would augment one's appreciation of music, but it would not create the liking for it in one who was not musically inclined. Changing one's boarding house might increase one's appreciation of food, but it is very doubtful whether it could make an epicure out of one who was inclined to ignore food or cause an established epicure to become indifferent to food. Suitable education might greatly increase one's pleasure in constructing things from metal or wood or thread (needlework), but it is doubtful whether it could create a liking for this type of activity in one who was disinclined.

One's want patterns no doubt change somewhat with age and circumstances. Nevertheless, it seems clear that these want patterns are to a very substantial degree based upon inborn characteristics. Think over the items which you rate as high. Were you *trained* to think these items important, and could you have been *trained* just as easily to think them unimportant and to substitute other items for them?

This game, it seems to me, throws considerable light on a number of questions which have been baffling, and raises some doubts about others which may formerly have been erroneously answered. For example, in some circles it is considered a sign of culture if one enjoys excellent cuisine and an indication of low breeding if one is not discriminating. Is this necessarily accurate? Sometimes we hear people in general upbraided because they do not get out to vote, do not write their congressmen and senators, do not concern themselves with political questions. Is it true that we all have the capacity to be equally interested, or does taste enter into the problem? Some people have mental patterns which make them enjoy philosophical discussions, others avoid them whenever possible. Is it the same with politics and for the same reason? If so, we should get acquainted with ourselves. Do not the extreme reactions of these ten individuals toward Ownership throw light on the problem (or perhaps we should say the non-existence) of *economic* man? Certainly, in the light of these differences, it is extremely hazardous to lump all humanity together in relation to economic operations and problems.

It seems very likely that anyone playing this game will be convinced of his own individuality. If groups will play the game together—striving for complete honesty—it is likely to alter materially their ideas about themselves. If the group is "uppity" and thinks of its members as being different from and better than their fellows, playing the game will go a long way toward demonstrating that all human beings are made of the same clay, but that, importantly, the pattern for each is different.

There are a number of specific ways in which this type of game could be used to advantage. The "want patterns" of congenial husbands and wives could be compared, also the patterns of those who have been divorced. Each individual would doubtless exhibit a distinctive pattern, but perhaps it would be possible to see "the fits" and "the misfits" and some of the basic reasons for congeniality or lack of it. For this particular purpose (as well as for other specific purposes) it might be well to expand the number of boxes and make the game more detailed. If significant findings should result from a study of congenial and noncongenial marriages, then the patterns of prospective mates determined before marriage could hardly fail to be important.

Acquaintance with and study of these and more extensive (or more intensive) patterns would be revealing in quite a different realm. Suppose you were a salesman: Would it not facilitate your operations if you were acquainted with the diversity of want patterns of those to whom you might be selling? Might it not help to know *what* to sell, if you had a realistic insight into the character and diversity of the want patterns of real people such as those with whom you deal? I believe that such insight ought effectively to supplement and partially replace the trial and error method whereby merchandise must often be tried on the public before its salability becomes known.

Looking at the matter in a broad way, most of us are salesmen: the minister or priest is selling religion (or his brand of it); the lawyer is selling his legal services; the physician, his medical care; the teacher is selling his education; the writer, his writings; the entertainer, his entertainment. The payments for these commodities are not by any means solely in the coin of the realm, but true salesmanship nevertheless is involved, and in every case it would be a tremendous help, so it seems to me, if the salesmen could recognize the individuality of every potential customer and could be acquainted with the diverse want patterns of the real people to whom he has to sell.

Our success in the whole field of human relations depends to a very great extent upon our understanding the want patterns of the individuals who make up society. Knowing what *man* wants cannot suffice, and those who are successful in human relations recognize this implicitly by their activities, if not verbally. Progress in human relations can come rapidly, as we learn—all of us—more and more about our want patterns and those of our fellows.

VII

Educational Assembly Line

IN THE PRECEDING chapters we have tried to set forth some of the most significant ways in which human beings exhibit differences (many of them to a substantial degree inborn). In the chapters which follow we will be concerned largely with the applications and implications of these differences as they appear to me. I lay no claim to being an expert in any of the diverse fields which need to be considered, but I am keenly aware of some of the facts of individuality and of the urgent need for their inclusion in the field of human knowledge.

It is extremely easy to sit back and find fault with almost any human institution or any human product. Our system of education is a favorite target because it is so broad in its scope, because it touches everyone's life, and because we all tend to have our own pet ideas on how to rectify the system's particular deficiencies which we feel may have kept us (or others) from realizing our greatest potentialities. These pet ideas, by the way, are in part the product of our own individual mental patterns and may have highly restricted application if they are based upon mental traits that are possessed by only a few, including ourselves. Humanity at large cannot be judged by any individual's yardstick.

In the discussion of this problem let it be understood all along that I do not pretend to have the answers, nor do I think the solution of educational problems easy. My discussion will be based upon the application of what I believe to be undeniable and highly pertinent facts, the recognition of which is often neglected—namely, that individual children have important inborn qualities which make them live in sensory worlds that are distinctive for each; that because of inherent patterns of intellectual potentialities they do not *think* alike nor do they *want* alike. I shall make no pretense of writing a well-rounded discussion of education, but shall point out some of the ways in which the facts of individuality impinge. What I have to say will be broadly constructive and not narrowly dogmatic.

In spite of the importance of the contrary view, I have sincere sympathy for educationalists who tend to accept the uniformity idea, and an appreciation for the reasons that underly their doing so. I believe strongly in education, and the uniformity idea certainly magnifies its importance. Furthermore, at first glance there appears to be considerable sense to the point of view held in substance by many educators: "Nothing can be done about a child's ancestry, but much can be done to develop his personality and life; therefore we will assume that the necessary seed has been planted, and will carry on from this point."

The fallacy in this point of view is this: Biological variability reaches its highest development in human beings. Enormously important inborn differences exist, and if individual children are taken for what they individually are, much more can be done for their personalities, since the basis of personality may be said to reside in the very fact of their inborn differences.

Some of the more seasoned educationalists will react to my thesis in this way: "Why are you making all this hullabaloo over something that everyone agrees to? Everyone knows that inheritance is of some importance."

My answer is this: Lip service is not enough; we must also *act* as if we believe that inheritance is important and that the variations resulting from combined inheritances are *the key to understanding* not only what a child is but what he may become. Keys are to be used; merely acknowledging vaguely that they may exist is a pleasant gesture, but it is futile. If children's inborn mental patterns are different in important ways, let's stop trying to educate them as though they were all substantially the same; let's find out how they are different and do something about it! We cannot ease ourselves away from educational problems by saying that the differences are "not *very* important." If the differences are not very important, then freedom is not very important and the idea of individual worth is not very important, and the Statue of Liberty who lifts her "lamp beside the golden door" of our democracy becomes only an antiquated metal object commemorating nothing.

To those who are complacent in the belief that education is living up to its responsibilities toward individual pupils, I would say: Whenever I see educators *seriously investigating, seriously trying to find out how children differ from one another,* I will agree that they believe in the nonuniformity doctrine and are laying a foundation for the real enlightenment and development of free men and women. As long as they neglect this, I will conclude that, in effect at least, they believe in the assembly-line doctrine which stultifies and deadens.

It may be well to ask ourselves these searching questions: "How successful has our school system been in the past in dealing with outstanding individuals? Are we making real strides in the current decades toward dealing with them more satisfactorily?"

If we go back over our history and select the names of Americans who in one field or another have made the greatest impact on the world I believe we could, with some justification, pick out the names of Benjamin Franklin, Abraham Lincoln, and Thomas Edison. Their school days, fortunately for our purpose, were spaced about fifty years or more apart, and we might look for gross improvement during the intervening decades. It is a striking fact, however, that not one of these greatest men received with any degree of relish the formal education that was offered in his day. Benjamin Franklin "was wholly self-taught as if he had never gone to school." Abraham Lincoln went to school a total of about a year "by littles." He left in his biographical notes this comment: "There were some schools, so-called—there was absolutely nothing to excite ambition for education." Thomas Edison, a couple of generations later (to use his own words), "was always at the foot of the class" during his short period of schooling.

Would we be able to do better by these individuals if they were in our schools today? I believe the answer might be yes, but the results would still be far from satisfactory because we do not yet recognize as we should the importance of individuality. In our talent scouting for brains, for example, we tend to search out those who make the highest grades in *all* the subjects on the assumption that the lump of dough concept of intelligence holds. By such a procedure we would not be able to spot Franklins, Lincolns, and Edisons because each had a distinct mental pattern. Even Franklin, the broad man of culture, did not take to Latin and arithmetic.

The fact that our schools have become almost universalized in their scope puts us at a disadvantage in dealing with highly exceptional individuals. Today the social pressure on every child to go to school—usually a public school—is very great as compared with what it was in the times of Franklin, Lincoln, and Edison. These exceptional individuals could, and did, duck formal education and go their own ways. Today the school regime would probably be less onerous to them, but they would be forced to stick with it.

It can be said, perhaps, that assembly-line education, modified slightly by individual demands, works passably for a large number of "common run" people, but that it falls down badly when it comes to exceptional individuals. Even if this generous interpretation is valid, the situation is most serious, especially when looked upon with historical perspective. Although obviously some individuals fall more easily into prescribed patterns than others, there is serious doubt in my mind whether there are really any "common run" people. Education, to be worthy of its root meaning, should expect to find each individual outstanding in some qualities that can be *educated*.

The problems of grades, degrees, promotion, recognition in general, maintaining morale, all enter into the operation of any school, and are by no means easy to solve. Taking individuality into account will certainly involve finding out more about the aptitudes of the individual children, so as to give each the kind of training he can accept. This does not mean that work and discipline should be left out or that all types of training should not mix, but it will mean that all children can respond with a moderate degree of success and that the sense of failure and frustration can be kept at a minimum.

My own disposition is to abolish much that is stereotyped in our educational system, and to place less emphasis on grades and degrees. Rules and regulations are to a degree necessary, but rules should be bent and broken whenever it seems necessary. I had the honor of making a motion which admitted to a university graduate school a scholar who had graduated neither from high school nor college. He was capable of doing scholarly work, however, and his subsequent record has justified the action.

We should not approach the problem of taking care of individuality without the recognition that in some ways it complicates matters greatly. If the assembly-line doctrine were valid and everyone could fit into the same pattern, the whole educational system could be built with machinelike precision—which, it may be said, seems to have been the aim of too many of our institutions. They sometimes resemble educational "factories" intent on turning out uniform products, and many cease to look upon themselves as seats of learning where *individuals* may come for the development and enrichment of their minds.

Recognition of the facts of life respecting biological variability demands that more time, effort, and money be spent on education than ever before, though with more particular effort and attention spent on the real needs of students and less on futile attempts to foster conformity, economies would result. The place of parents and homes in the educational process will likely be magnified and formal schooling may be diminished or substantially altered. Who knows?

It is to be devoutly hoped that education as a professional activity will constitute more of a challenge than it has in recent years, and that the people with the greatest aptitude for educational work will be attracted. Certainly it calls for the highest abilities possible, and these are not always possessed by the best lesson getters. Too often education, in the professional sense, appears to be a last resort. I know a man who in his youth tried to go into medicine but couldn't make the grade; then he tried law and couldn't make it. Finally he tried education and became relatively successful. It could be that a man lacking aptitudes for medicine and law has just what it takes in the field of education. One cannot avoid the suspicion, however, that in many cases of this kind the ability to succeed in education is based upon lower standards of performance in that field. Certainly it appears that many who might do well in education are finding a greater challenge, and greater opportunities, in other fields.

What specifically can be done to improve education and bring it more in line with the facts of human life and with American ideals of freedom and individual worth?

One immediate innovation would be to start teaching children, even as early as the preschool years, about their own individuality. Even at an early age their senses of taste and smell, their reactions to colors and art, their ways of doing things, and their likes and dislikes in stories, etc., will be sufficiently diverse as to be striking and revealing. Some problems would be created by following this type of activity up through the grades, but it should be an antidote for the contagious disease of which the symptoms are a craving to be "average, normal, and secure." If the idea of nonuniformity were clearly demonstrated to children at an early age it would become an easily accepted commonplace. Children react quickly to innovation, and the healthy attitude incident to individuality and love of liberty could readily replace the diseased outlook which extols the "normal."

As a student progresses through school he should continuously learn more and more about himself and more and more about the society into which he has to fit (or misfit, if need be). The chances of his being a misfit will be vastly decreased if he *knows* about himself and about society. The truth does not bind and fetter people; it sets them free. If, under this new approach to education which I think is ultimately inevitable, an individual finds himself with a pattern of abilities or interests that seems highly unusual, he will be more inclined to take his unusualness as a matter of course and will not be psychologically disturbed.

As a result of a program of this kind, at least some of the children will early find their interests and what is to be their future occupation. Some will be justified in abandoning their formal schooling earlier and will be better off for the change. Others will be inclined toward further education along practical as well as technical lines. As a result, their academic careers will be modified, though not necessarily cut short. We will probably find that extensive book learning is by no means a desirable goal for everyone, and we will have more sympathy for the sage who said, "I would prefer not being able to read and write, than being able to do nothing but read and write."

One of the challenges which the writing of *The Human Frontier* has brought to me repeatedly during the past seven years is this: "Show us examples (*or an example*) of how people have been studied from every angle, with the result that their difficulties have been eliminated." Unfortunately such studies have never been carried out, and so examples are out of the question. I wish I did know of examples in the field of education, in which an individual's differences have been ascertained and the findings applied as I think they might be!

I can think of one young man who strikingly exemplified the need for the recognition of individual patterns—one who was destined on the basis of his school performance to be a rank failure. This young man had an excellent personality and was very well liked by all who knew him, including his teachers. It was because of this that he was able eventually to graduate from high school; everyone knew he was "dumb," but high school standards are often low or flexible and he got the necessary grades somehow and was awarded a diploma.

When time came for college he tried several times—not only was he unable to graduate, he was not able to do well enough to stay in school for more than a year. Always the report was, "We like him but he can't do college work." Eventually and without the help of schools of any kind—the schools in fact had branded him a failure and had stood in the way of his finding himself—the young man actually found himself. It is certain now that he was not "dumb" at all, just able along unconventional lines. He turned out to be mechanically ingenious and inventive, and is now the head of a large and growing business which is based largely upon his own inventiveness, coupled with his unusual ability to get along with people. I hope for the day when schools will help such people rather than stand in their way! This day cannot come until we recognize that *patterns* exist in everyone and that the lump-of-dough idea of intelligence, which is encountered often enough to sour those whose patterns show strong contrasts, is dumped into the garbage.

Perhaps most important of all, teaching the facts of individuality to children will foster in them a love of freedom, an appreciation of their fellows, and an ability to work and play harmoniously with others.

There is a tendency to think that becoming acquainted with *differences* will lead to disharmony. I believe the opposite is true. Let us imagine, if you will, an experiment involving two similar families, each, we'll say, with three children. Every item of existence in these imaginary families is the same except that the children in one family are taught by precept and example as follows: "You children are all alike. What one likes the rest should like; what one does, the others should do. Be *normal* children." The children in the other family are taught thusly: "Each of you children is distinctive; each will have some different likes and dislikes. You will not always want to do the same things. Learn to understand each other; respect each other's individuality."

In which family do you think there will be greater harmony? I believe the answer is obvious and that a sentimental neglect of the biological variability that resides in human beings (in the hope that such neglect will foster better relations between them) is a well-meaning but worse than futile gesture. A *dual*-control electrically heated blanket in a home is not a sign of disharmony; it recognizes differences and by so doing promotes *harmony*.

It would be unfortunate if my remarks were construed as neglectful of the work of John Dewey and many others who have recognized the problem of individuality and have sought to meet it with "progressive" schools and other expedients. It would also be unfortunate if I should make the problems seem easy. My contribution is to emphasize, as effectively as I can, how great and all-pervading human differences are, how we need to know vastly more about them—also to make it clear that the function of education is not to abolish these differences.

Closely related to the teaching of individuality is the need to set some of our thinking straight. Unfortunately some of the thinking that is askew has been fostered in the teaching of natural science, including biology. Science is always interested in generalizations—hypotheses, theories, laws—which grow out of observations. Induction is followed by deduction.

Because the facts of biological variability as they are related to human beings have not been adequately appreciated and have been taught even less adequately, there is a strong presumption that "getting scientific" concerning human beings consists in making all-inclusive generalizations about them. This is understandable because scientists make generalizations about everything else that they study. The crux of the difficulty lies in the fact that the generalizations which have been made about human beings in the past are premature. Sufficient induction has not preceded the deductions. Generalizations which lump all humanity together are likely to be either trivial or entirely misleading. A real science of man must be built upon *extended* observations, and there is every likelihood that in relation to every specific problem men will be found to belong in different categories—not lumped together.

We will have to give up a substantial amount of interest in "the individual," because he is an abstraction, a hypothetical, generalized being with the taint of an assembly line, to whom universal statements apply. We will have to trade off this interest for an interest in *individuals*. These are not abstractions; they are real. They are not hypothetical, but actual; specific, not generalized; distinctive, not standardized; and to them relatively few universal statements apply. We will cease to stress the attributes of the *mind of man*, and learn more about the *minds of men*.

As will be made clearer in a later chapter, statistical studies have limitations and, where patterns are concerned, averaging won't work. We will have to learn that "being statistical" (and interested in averages) and "being scientific" are not synonymous expressions.

Of course, before children can be led to learn the most about themselves, a large mass of information about individual differences and their meaning will have to be accumulated. This puts a very large and urgent assignment on the natural scientists and those that support their investigations, to put their talents and money to work in the development of a real "science of man." This calls for interdisciplinary research and for a degree of cooperation between all natural scientists and psychologists that has hitherto not been attained. Better and better insights will be developed as time goes on, and these will make possible improved adjustments. I certainly am not proposing that education and educators go off half-cocked and jump at hasty conclusions as to pupils' endowments or give all sorts of half-baked counseling advice.

A prominent leader in education indicated to me that in his opinion by far the major part of current "educational research" is done, not with the hope of finding anything very significant, but rather to conform to the prevailing mode and to impress one's associates. "As a result, the research is getting absolutely nowhere," he said. A large number of doctoral theses are written every year dealing with current procedures in particular localities—organizational details, specialized curricula, transportation problems, minor improvements, application of test batteries to forecasting scholarship, accreditation problems, interscholastic athletics, how to choose text books, etc., etc. There appears to be an alarming paucity of topics which might be regarded as having far-reaching implications or as laying a foundation for the future. One is reminded of the scriptural saying, "Where there is no vision the people perish."

Could not a substantial amount of the effort that goes into these studies be redirected toward the objective of getting acquainted with the *real children* whom schools serve? Human variability in the field of the senses is so great that Blakeslee has said ". . . different people live in different worlds so far as their sensory reactions are concerned." Are not these differences in seeing, hearing, tasting, smelling, detection of heat and cold and pressure worthy of note? Why not learn something about small children's likes and dislikes in the field of art? Why not study the reading problems (probably different for each child) in a half-dozen children? Why not explore in a truly inductive manner the mental patterns of people—a few at a time? Once this type of investigation is initiated, all kinds of possibilities will immediately come to the fore, and all the information gained will be of the type that will help gain the insight into real people that is so sorely needed.

Major discoveries in education are exceedingly difficult to make, because in order to be "major" it has been traditionally decreed that they have to apply to everyone. If one could find, for example, a new, improved, and universally applicable method for teaching people how to read effectively, this would be considered a major discovery. In view of the great biological variability which exists, it may be seriously doubted whether any such method exists. The best method for some is not the best method for others, and perhaps stopping the search for universal best methods would be the best way to progress. More modest findings applicable to perhaps a small percentage of the population would be within the reach of educational investigators and would contribute to the fulfillment of a real need.

This is another variation of the problem of premature generalized thinking. We have lived too long with the idea that there must be a best way for *man* to do everything. We have said that either everyone should eat a heavy breakfast or else no one should. If light of a particular intensity or quality is best for some children, it is best for all. If lots of reading is good for some children, it is good for all. If eight hours sleep is right for some people, it is right for all. If some adults get along without much physical exercise, then no one needs very much. All these generalizations are premature and probably completely unwarranted. We need to approach the facts with a mind that is willing to understand that one man's meat *is* another's poison, and that it is possible to cease advocating poison for any man.

In the field of education it is highly desirable, from the practical standpoint, that pupils be grouped together in classes and that uniform procedures be applied whenever they can without doing violence to the individuality of the children. It is partly for this reason that it is so important to *know* how children are alike and how they are different. We can then gauge when they can be handled groupwise, how many groups are necessary or desirable, and when individual attention is needed.

More difficulties have arisen in connection with school regimentation than we probably realize. In olden times muscle was often used to hold the bigger boys in line, and one of the qualifications of a teacher was that he be able to thrash the biggest (and often the most backward) pupil. In some respects the situation has greatly improved, in that children start to school earlier and stay with schooling more consistently. Juvenile delinquency and crime among the teen agers is, however, a terrific problem and one which is not growing less important. It is my well-considered opinion that much crime and delinquency (as well as an appreciable amount of mental disease) is a direct revolt against assembly-line schooling, with its incapacity for taking care of and fitting for life those whose interests and capabilities lie outside the traditional school subjects. It has been demonstrated many times that people who do not adjust well to ordinary school work may nevertheless be extraordinarily able, and this is often true of criminals.

If we knew better than we do at present how children are alike and how they differ, we would be able to judge to what extent crime, delinquency, and mental disease are due to assembly-line education and to what extent other causes operate. The crime and mental diseases bills, both from the human standpoint and from the monetary standpoint, are so stupendous and hinge on juvenile upbringing to such an extent that we can ill afford to neglect any promising approach.

In the present serious conflict of ideologies in our world it is not enough to blindly criticize (and sometimes fear) the Communists; we must in our own democracy demonstrate with real affirmation the bases of what we mean by freedom. If we continue to assume that all "normal" children are alike and teach them accordingly, we are contributing to the too-prevalent tendency toward regimentation which can make any people easy prey to dictatorship. If, however, we want to foster the love of freedom, we will teach as if we really believed in individuality and its importance to free men; we will teach the children about individuality; we will ourselves seek to learn more about it, and we will accommodate as well as we can the education that we give to the needs of individual pupils.

VIII

When Can We Regiment?

WHEN WE KNOW more about people, particularly in what specific ways they are alike and in what ways different, we will be incomparably more effective in making and enforcing rules and laws governing their conduct. Whenever we put laws on the statute books that cannot be enforced, which is very often, we create disrespect for law and run the risk of making lawbreakers out of people who would otherwise be law-abiding citizens.

A classic example of a law which we found we couldn't enforce was the Prohibition Amendment, which was placed in our Constitution and then repealed. Thomas Jefferson had said nearly 150 years before, "Tastes cannot be controlled by law," and had in this statement demonstrated great wisdom and insight. *Why* cannot tastes be controlled by law? Because there is a wide diversity of tastes which are not simply trained into people (as is often thought) but are based upon inborn differences of a profound and basic nature. People would have to be changed fundamentally (genetically) before these tastes could be governed by law. If we all had the same tastes or if we were perfectly adaptable in them, one of two things would have happened: either the Eighteenth Amendment would never have been put on the books (we would have agreed on the use of alcoholic beverages), or it would have stayed there and would have been enforced, because we would have adapted ourselves to the new regime.

People differ in their attitudes toward alcoholic beverages for many different reasons—sensory, physiological, psychological—which do not involve the question of mores. To illustrate how this can be so, let us consider for example why people's attitudes toward food differ so greatly. Here mores are involved very little if at all. As we saw in Chapter VI some individuals give food a top rating as a source of life satisfaction. Others give it a zero rating. No moral judgment is involved but the difference is there just the same, and it would be difficult to imagine an epicure's being trained to care nothing for food, or the transformation of a person who is completely indifferent to food into an epicure. It is a fact, which must have its basis in inborn differences, that for a substantial number of people alcoholic beverages rate as *an important reason for living*, and the ignoring of this was the fundamental weakness of the Prohibition Amendment.

Other statutes which are continually broken by people who are temperamentally not actually in the "lawbreaker" class are the speed laws. We often set a limit of twenty miles per hour in cities, but if anyone drives that slowly on many streets, he finds he is actually holding up traffic. Why are suitable speed laws so hard to make and to enforce? A small part of the difficulty lies in the differences in automobiles, but mostly it is because drivers are so different. They have different tastes as to speed; they have vastly different skills. Again, if we were all alike or completely adaptable we could set almost any speed limit we chose and everyone would abide by it. As it is, some drivers can, and actually do, break the law practically all of the time, and still are safer than most other drivers.

There are many physiological and even anatomical factors which enter into the determination of how fast and how skillfully a person will drive. Reaction times make a difference; ability to judge speeds, facility of eye movements, peripheral vision, muscular coordination—all of these are important, as is also the fact that some people appear to be constitutionally the hurrying kind, while for others leisureliness is the general rule of their lives. In addition there are mental and emotional traits that enter—the gambling spirit, willingness to take a chance, the ability or inability to concentrate, and the tendency to become angry. A recent study has shown that automobile accidents have a way of happening when people are angry, and if this is so, placid individuals are much more likely to be safe drivers. All of these variabilities make it impossible to force the same rules on everyone and make them stick.

Gambling is another area in which lawmaking and law enforcement are relatively unsuccessful. In at least one state I believe it has been actually against the law to play cards at all, and in others a game of penny ante played in one's own home is illegal. Pool halls, primarily because of their gambling associations, are outlawed in some localities, as are also horse and dog racing. It would appear that laws of this kind cannot be enforced for a whole population, and that the gambling evil which is real must be met by laws that strike at the evil and yet are enforceable.

The desire to gamble, at least for small stakes, is very widespread. In the group of ten people whose life's satisfactions we explored in an earlier chapter, betting rated thirtieth among the forty-eight items. For some groups, it would doubtless rate much higher. If a substantial proportion of people think that betting is one of the important reasons for living, then we had better watch our step when we try to legislate it out of existence.

It is a fact, of course, that the total number of people who place small bets on every conceivable type of game or contest is enormous. Why this urge exists is an interesting question. For a vast majority of these people the monetary gains or losses are trifling in the extreme and cannot be a measure of the enjoyment. I suspect that betting even a trifling sum on a football game allows the bettor to get *into the game* in a sense that would not ordinarily be possible otherwise. Competitive activity is highly attractive to some people, and getting the best of a friend on an election bet may have an attraction for this reason. Whatever the psychological traits that enter into the desire, I am convinced that the betting urge is not something that can be trained into or out of people at will. If it were solely a matter of training, anti-betting laws could be made and enforced.

Nothing that I have said should be taken to indicate that I condone the evils that arise out of gambling. It is precisely because I would like to see the gambling evil abolished as far as is possible that I plead for an understanding of the betting urge. This we cannot understand, I feel sure, if we leave individuality out of the problem and assume that training is the whole answer.

It is obvious that there are many kinds of laws which *because of fundamental differences in people* could not be enforced if we had any reason to want to enforce them. For example, we would encounter terrific resistance if we tried to set a time for everyone to go to bed, or for everyone to rise; if we tried to insist that every son should follow an occupation approved by his father; if we should prescribe what people should eat or not eat; if we should tell them they must own their own home before buying a television set; or that they must write right-handed; or that a red-headed man must not marry a red-headed girl. All of these items involve matters of taste or ways in which people differ tremendously one from another. Fortunately none of these regulations is at present on any statute books, so far as I know. But no one of them is basically more foolish or futile than certain laws we do have, and attitudes behind these laws. As long as we divide mankind into two groups, the *normal* and the *abnormal*, we risk passing unrealistic laws; and as long as we blind ourselves to the relationship between conduct and inherited physical and mental patterns, we are in danger of demanding laws that try to improve conduct by asserting in effect: *I* know what is best for *you* because I know what "normal man" wants and should have —*I* am normal and *you* should be too.

It is equally obvious that there are numerous regulations which are generally enforceable because they do not seriously violate any distinctive tastes or involve wide differences between people. We can tell people to drive on the right side of the highway (or on the left in Britain); to give their children a minimum of education; to let their neighbors sleep at night; to avoid marrying close relatives; to pay a minimum wage to their employees; to put on clothing before appearing in public places; and while there may be occasional violations, the regulations find general acceptance and do not become dead letters.

It behooves us to know, before we can make satisfactory laws, in what areas people can and cannot be regulated—also why and why not. For instance, if we began telling people how they are to earn a living, difficulties would certainly mount. People's aptitudes are so diverse that forcing them to do something that they are not fitted for becomes difficult. We have come to regard it as one of our inalienable rights to decide what our occupations shall be. If we cannot choose our own work, we regard ourselves as slaves, even though at a task of our own choosing we might work even harder. The great increase in industrialization in the United States since 1900 has made it less easy for men to choose their own occupations according to aptitudes, as was possible, theoretically at least, in the days of handicraft. But even though his choice may be a limited one, a man still wants it to be his *own* choice.

In the military services it is essential that there be discipline and obedience and a certain amount of disregard for the likes and dislikes of the soldiers themselves. Actually, however, there have been serious attempts, and they will doubtless increase, to get individual members of the armed services into lines of work which will be least distasteful. That the military services have not been entirely successful in selecting men for different types of work should be admitted. There are many kinds of work to be done in the service, and obviously in the interest of efficiency misfits (in respect to the job to be done) should be eliminated as far as is possible. Here is of course an interesting clue for us as civilians: If for the purposes of war it is important to make "misfits" into "fits" by gaining insight into the differing capabilities of people, may it not be even more vital to do so for the purposes of peace?

In general, restrictions placed upon any of our activities—travel, building homes, buying or operating automobiles, renting property, installment buying, food purchasing, etc.—are bound to be enforced with difficulty if they invade, to too great an extent, the desire of people to follow their own tastes. Difficulty in the enforcement of necessary regulations will be encountered, too, if the reasons for the regulations are not made clear in a way that will take account of this desire.

Let us suppose that there is a coffee shortage, and that we make it unlawful for anyone to have more than the equivalent of one cup a day, and we ration coffee to adults on this basis. The provisions of this restriction come very close to doing what Jefferson said could not be done —"controlling tastes by law." What will be the result? A black market in coffee will develop, and respectable people who have come to depend upon coffee several times a day will get more than the law allows in spite of anything that the government can do.

Black markets are a natural phenomenon which seem to be inevitable and are occasioned to a large degree by people's differences in tastes and their differences with respect to the diligence and ability they exercise in trying to satisfy their wants. When tastes for such things as coffee, alcoholic drinks, or tobacco are concerned, mere laws will not regulate or uniformly spread out their use.

Another area in which regulation causes dissatisfaction and great wastage of manpower is that of work loads. People's work capacities along specific lines vary tremendously, and whenever a union restriction stipulates, for example, that a bricklayer cannot lay more than so many bricks a day, it asks the fast worker to live a lie, makes him less happy with his work, and sacrifices his greater productivity. Under nonrestrictive conditions a fast worker will accommodate himself somewhat to the pace of his fellow workers, and in certain kinds of operations, is bound to help slower members of the team. This is probably as it should be.

In all walks of life, men exhibit wide divergencies in their efficiency, and a substantial amount of the differences are based on inborn capabilities. Shall we amputate the excess efficiency that some have and bring everyone down to the level of the least efficient? This does not seem to make sense. Certainly in some fields it would be disastrous.

When we place every worker on the same level of pay regardless of how much or how well he works, or insist on bringing the most effective down to the level of the least effective, we are actually confessing, at considerable cost, that *we don't know how to gauge a worker's value.* To level down the more effective workers is an easy way out, but it would be much more in accord with the ideal of democracy if the less effective could be made more so, or else transferred to some other work where he could excel and enjoy his work more, at the same time allowing efficient workers to get more than the minimum wage which every worker should obtain.

Retirement at sixty-five (or at some other uniformly fixed age) is a product of assembly-line thinking. If people were born alike, everyone ought to be ready to retire (if at all) at the same age. Oliver Wendell Holmes, the late jurist, Alonzo Stagg, the football coach, and John Dewey, the philosopher, have demonstrated that the sixty-five year limit is off *in some cases* by nearly twenty-five years.

What enables some individuals to maintain their efficiency much longer than others is practically unknown, because aging has never been studied sufficiently on an individual basis. We have been too interested in learning how *man* ages, to be expert on the subject of how *men* age.

No adequate means of measuring physiological or psychological age has been developed. It is a fact, however, that longevity runs in families, and there can be no doubt that patterns of inheritance come into play. The possibilities of applying nutritional knowledge to the problem of prolonging the useful life of those whose genetic make-up is not wholly favorable will be discussed briefly in a later chapter.

I agree, in summary, that regimentation is to a degree necessary. In a complicated social structure we need regulations for efficiency and smooth running, but if they are carried too far without an understanding of human variation, revolt is likely to be stirred up and carried over even to the *necessary* rules. If we were all born alike and adaptable we could stand an indefinite amount of regulation. How much we can stand depends on how important our differences are. If they were negligible we should not need to worry about carrying regimentation too far, but inasmuch as our differences are great, we must adhere to our democratic ideals and resist the excessive encroachment of regimentation on our lives. Along lines in which we show small differences we can take regimentation; along lines in which we have large differences we must have freedom!

IX

What Liars Can't Figure

I HOPE THAT my statistician friends, of whom I have several, will not take offense at the jocular title of this chapter or at anything that is in it. It may seem unfair to approach the subject of statistics negatively when much can be written on the positive side. Statistics and statisticians are essential to modern life and volumes could be written on the subject of what they *can* do.

In an age where manufacturing, transportation, and, to an increasing extent, agriculture and many other human activities are based upon *experiments*, the basic importance of the principles of statistics can hardly be overrated, because these principles are present inherently in almost any experiment, and many experiments cannot be rightly planned or interpreted without their use. A modern view of the use of statistics not only recognizes its function in bringing order out of a chaotic mass of numerical data, but also its application of statistical principles to the planning of experiments which will yield valid answers with a minimum of effort. Without statistics modern industrial life could not exist.

There are some areas with which we are concerned, however, in which statistical methods are relatively impotent, and where they must be used if at all with great caution. If Mr. Die V. Hard who is 50 years old goes to an insurance agent he may find that the "life expectancy" of a man in the United States of this age is 21.37 years but the insurance agent can offer him no assurance that he individually will live even half that long nor can it be denied that he may live twice that long.

Actually it would be possible to limit the calculations and include not all fifty-year-olds but only a selected group—for instance, those whose parents and grandparents all lived to be 80 years old. Another selected group could be fifty-year-olds who have high blood pressure. For the high blood pressure group the life expectancy would be less than 21.37 years, and for the group whose forebears had long life the expectancy would be more than 21.37 years. By narrowing the group on other specified bases, it would be possible to calculate for a smaller and smaller number what the life expectancy would be, but the final group would still have to be large enough to represent an adequate sample and it would be impossible to calculate for an individual case.

We thus see one fundamental limitation of statistics with respect to individual people. Statistics deal with groupings of individuals and their central tendencies: averages, medians, and modes, also with ranges, deviations, etc., but not with any single individual. As we will see more clearly later, *individuals* play a tremendous part in the development of history (international, national, local, or personal) and it is beyond the scope of statistics to predict or interpret their individual actions.

When statistical methods are used to predict as to the future, predictions are always based upon present and past conditions. Election polls are valid, at best, for the group represented and at the time of the poll. No actuarial methods are capable of predicting whether or when great medical advances, which may still further prolong life, will be made. Actually fifty-year-olds as of today may, on the average, live materially longer than 21.37 years as a result of medical discoveries yet to be made. But statistics can know nothing of this except as it is foreshadowed by the past.

Probably more important than those limitations, especially as related to the theme of this book, is the limitation in the ability to deal with the *patterns* that enter into the make-up of every individual person. As has been set forth in previous chapters, all of us have distinctive patterns—anatomically (even grossly we do not have exactly the same number of muscles and bones in our bodies), neurologically, endocrinologically, mentally, and with respect to our life satisfactions. In a later chapter we will discuss our distinctive metabolic patterns.

The difficulty of dealing with patterns statistically is obvious when we consider that there is no way of averaging together several rug patterns, for example, and getting a meaningful result. The average of a number of different patterns might turn out to be no pattern at all. If we were able to average together the patterns of the footprints of a large number of animals, including fowls, we would probably end up with a circular shape which would be meaningless and representative of nothing. If we were to average together all the feet of the human male adult population (which obviously would make more sense since human feet do resemble each other) we would find that a shoe built to fit this average foot would fit less than 5 per cent of the adult male population. Even when averaging is possible, the results are not necessarily useful.

The limitations of averaging will be made clearer if we consider, for example, a large bag of assorted marbles, which we may wish to describe. The average size of the marbles will be a measurable and meaningful quantity; also the average weight, the average density, the average hardness. But let us turn to the attribute of color. The marbles in the bag are of assorted colors—red, blue, green, brown, mottled, striped, milky, metallic (steel), and what not. The only way to strike an average would be to mount an adequate sampling on a disk and whirl the disk rapidly, noting the color—which would likely be a dirty gray. Then we can conclude, can we, that the average marble is dirty gray? Not at all, for there isn't a dirty gray marble in the whole bag!

Color is not the only thing that might give us trouble in our averaging. Take composition for example. Suppose that some of the marbles are glass, some are plastic, and some are steel. If we analyze an adequate sampling we might come out with an answer like this: "The average marble is part glass, part plastic, and part steel." This is entirely erroneous because no marble has this composition, and it would be virtually impossible to make one according to these specifications.

Let us turn now more specifically to the problem of averaging human beings and planning on the basis of averages. The average height of human beings has some meaning, and this value, along with some knowledge as to the wideness of the variability, is used (perhaps somewhat unconsciously) in designing the height of doors. If doors are built so that, say, 9,999 persons out of 10,000 can pass through without stooping, the results are reasonably satisfactory. The average weight of human beings is also meaningful. In the earlier days of airplane transportation it was customary to weigh each individual in, and thus determine the aggregate plane load. Nowadays this is not done, and at least some airplane companies use the figure 150 pounds as the average. This is a useful figure and allows for a reasonably accurate calculation of the load.

With respect to individual measurable items, averages for human beings exist and may be useful. (In the case of the average shoe size, however, we have indicated that it is practically useless.) When we come to consider several items, averages exist for each but *not for the items taken together*. Let us suppose for purposes of illustration that we are concerned with only five items that enter into each person's make-up, and that each of these items can be measured on a quantitative basis: head size, talkativeness, arithmetical facility, sex urge, emotional stability.

People who are average as to head size could readily be found, likewise people who are average with respect to any one of the other items. If we try to find an individual who is average as to head size and also average as to talkativeness, the search is likely to be exhausting since such individuals will be relatively rare. If we seek to find an individual who has average head size, is average as to talkativeness and also average as to arithmetical facility, the task will be exceedingly difficult. If we add to our requirements that the individual shall also be average as to sex urge and average as to emotional stability, the search becomes impossible. In this illustration we have chosen only a few items of the large number that enter into the distinctive make-up of every individual. If more items are considered the probability of anyone being average in all is vanishingly small. It is in this sense we can say with considerable assurance that *the average human being does not exist,* e.g., one who is average in respect to every item in his make-up. In our study of metabolic patterns, which is discussed in a later chapter, the impossibility of finding an "average person" is further elucidated.

Not only are human beings unaverageable, their faces, their eyes, their personalities, their minds are likewise complex and incapable of being averaged. If we insist on trying to average such complex items, which we unconsciously do when we talk about "the human personality" or "the human mind" or "the child," we come out with concepts as misleading as we do with the marbles—the average, a dirty gray and made partly of plastic, partly of glass, and partly of steel. If we proceed with a group of colorful marbles and average their colors, we abolish all the color. If we average together a group of colorful personalities, we abolish all their color too. If we average a series of mental patterns, we abolish all patterns.

Any social planning which is done on the basis of the concept of the hypothetical average man had better be scrutinized very carefully for this fundamental error. Undeniably we tend to plan for colorless people (when actually they are colorful) and for patternless minds (when actually they all have very distinct patterns). A failure to appreciate how diverse our patterns are is, to my mind, the basis for our lack of progress in the field of understanding human nature and for our relative impotence in our dealing with human problems.

Classification of human beings, particularly, I believe, *with respect to specific problems*, is a necessity and is bound to come. To develop this ability to classify we shall have to use all the statistical prowess that is available—and more. In the meantime let us beware of thinking in terms of abstract *man, man's mind, man's wants, man's personality,* lest we fall into the error of calling dirty gray that which is colorful.

X

Find Your Own Food Fad

THERE ARE CERTAIN elementary laws about nutrition from which there is no escape. One is that we derive energy (measured in calories) from food and we cannot get any more energy out of a food than there is in it; another is that in addition to calories we need for health-giving nutrition other nutrients: minerals, amino acids (from proteins), vitamins, etc. No diet can yield good health if it is lacking in even a single one of the numerous essential elements.

"Nutritional needs" are actually the essential raw materials which an organism needs to build and maintain itself. For each species of mammal, for example, the list of needs is somewhat different, because in each species the chemical manufacturing machinery is somewhat different. Human beings and experimental rats have nutritional needs that are surprisingly similar in many ways (this illustrates the unity of the biological kingdom), but it is easy to devise a diet on which rats will thrive but on which human beings will surely die. Rats inherit from their rat ancestors the chemical machinery which allows them to make vitamin C (ascorbic acid) from sugars. Human beings do not inherit this machinery, and as a result they will contract scurvy and die rather promptly unless at least a small amount of ascorbic acid (an essential chemical for both rats and humans) is present in their diets.

Applying the fundamental principles of nutrition to one's self leads to asking the questions: How many calories (per day) do I need? How much calcium (or iron or iodine) do I need? How much of each of the essential amino acids do I need? How much of the various vitamins do I need? To these questions there is no easy answer, because each of us is an individual and as such has inherited metabolic (chemical) machinery that is somewhat distinctive. There is no assurance that we all need the *same amounts* of calcium, iron, leucine (one of the essential amino acids), vitamin A, thiamin, etc. In fact on the basis of what has been learned in recent years regarding the relationship between genetics and biochemical machinery it seems inescapable that each distinctive individual has a pattern of needs that is quantitatively different from that of his fellows. The various chemical processes that take place in our bodies do so with unequal efficiencies (for genetic reasons), and our needs for the various raw materials are quantitatively unequal for this reason.

It is quantitative differences in individual needs that constitute the basis, we believe, of the fact that certain human beings are vulnerable to the disease of alcoholism while others are not. The needs of the vulnerable individuals for certain of the food elements appear to be high, and when they drink alcohol and crowd out of their diet the minerals, amino acids, and vitamins, they become seriously deficient. This deficiency causes, in some way not well understood, a craving for more alcohol. Other individuals whose needs for the same food elements are relatively low can violate many of the rules of nutrition without becoming deficient or developing any alcoholic craving. This subject will be discussed further in the following chapter.

An acceptance of the idea that any man's needs are exactly like those of any other simplifies nutrition just as it does other fields; it also misleads, for it denies that what is one man's meat is ever another man's poison, and affirms that a nutritional observation which holds for one individual must hold for all.

Without consciously being aware of it, many people do accept the assembly-line doctrine as it applies to nutrition and assume without proof or evidence that what is good for some must of necessity be good for others. Food fads more often than not have been started by individuals who have believed that they have made discoveries regarding their own nutrition, and then have wished to extend their food practices to everyone on the assumption that what fits one fits all. Possibly such individuals do not actually believe that everyone is alike, but they, like the rest of us, enjoy pampering their egos, and do so by persuading others to imitate them.

There are, aside from the general principles already mentioned, few generalizations in the field of nutrition which apply to everyone. Let us consider, for example, the admonition, "One must always be careful to eat balanced meals including plenty of fresh vegetables and dairy products." While following this recommendation is not likely to do any well person harm, it cannot with assurance be given dogmatically as a requisite for everyone. Many people go through adult life and remain well even though they pay very little attention to what they eat or how much. Their automatic regulatory mechanisms apparently work well enough to satisfy their relatively efficient bodies. Such people apparently can afford to scoff at vitamins, calories, and everything else connected with nutrition during their whole adult life. How they would have fared if their mothers had violated the principles of good nutrition while they were children might be another question.

It is true that alcohol, sugar, and all refined foods are in a fundamental sense enemies of good nutrition, because they tend (in proportion to the amount used) to crowd important minerals, amino acids, and vitamins out of the diet. But it is undeniably true that some people are nevertheless able to consume relatively large amounts of these and still live to a ripe old age relatively free from disease.

Even for these hardy individuals, the general principles of nutrition hold; they have an absolute need for every mineral, amino acid, and vitamin, but their needs for certain crucial ones are probably low, and on top of this they probably have specific appetites which function automatically and which take care rather satisfactorily, under prevalent living conditions, of their bodily needs.

To these fortunate individuals (especially after they reach adulthood) it may be sufficient to say, "Follow your own cravings and tastes and you will be all right." But such advice would be extremely bad medicine for other people who have crucial needs that are high, or who lack sound self-regulatory appetites. An alcoholic is an extreme example; when he follows his own tastes and cravings, he inevitably ruins his life.

Such specific maxims as, "Avoid fried, greasy foods," are not by any means applicable to everyone. Some people whose digestive systems are relatively troublesome in other ways can tolerate fat very well indeed (like Jack Sprat's wife) and should not by any means be denied it, especially if they are not overweight.

A maxim such as, "Eat more roughage," is, of course, a good one for those who need it. But those whose insides are ruffled up and irritated by roughage, and who have no tendency toward constipation anyway, had better observe the opposite advice, "Eat less roughage."

"Eat plenty of uncooked fruit and vegetables," is advice that some people should follow. There appear to be some values in uncooked foods that we do not yet know fully about. However, this advice for some people would be very bad advice; it might be better for them if they avoided uncooked foods entirely.

"Drink a quart (or pint) of milk a day," is advice which many people should heed. Milk has nutritional values, particularly with respect to minerals and amino acids and certain vitamins, which make it very valuable. But for some unknown reason, milk does not agree with everybody, and these unfortunates should not punish themselves by drinking milk, but should find substitute foods (meat and vegetables, for example) which will supply the same food elements.

Nor can the time of eating be prescribed for everyone alike. When I see well-meaning statements such as, "Breakfast is your most important meal," I understand that the one who originated the statement accepts tacitly the uniformity doctrine and has probably found that for *himself* the statement is true. There are those, however, who get along better with a very light breakfast followed by a good lunch. Under some circumstances and for some people it is doubtless advantageous to eat a good breakfast and avoid lunch altogether, but for others to follow this pattern would be wholly unsatisfactory.

The admonition, "Never eat between meals," is another one which may be good for some people and bad for others. The same is true of "Drink a warm drink before retiring," or "A little whiskey is good for you after 50."

It is important for those who have difficulties with their digestive systems, including constipation, or who suffer from any one of a large number of diseases which may have a nutritional origin, to learn about their own individual needs. This can be done with some success by intelligent trial and observation, preferably with the help of a physician who is not bound by the uniformity doctrine. Further research on individual needs will make possible greater success.

Deficiencies with respect to minerals, vitamins, and amino acids are things to be looked for. All of these components are needed by every cell of one's body; hence there is no part of the body which may not misbehave due to a deficiency of this sort. If certain minerals are insufficient in amount in spite of the consumption of a well-rounded, diversified diet, they can be supplied in suitable form in drugstore preparations. If some of the numerous vitamins are needed in larger amounts, they too can be purchased. Intelligent interest and attention must be devoted to the choice of what supplements to take, while one bears in mind that quantities are of prime importance. It is not how *many* vitamins or minerals you take, but how *much* of each, that makes the difference.

People should not put reliance on liver extracts, yeast extracts, leaf extracts, molasses residues, or any such "natural" sources to yield the various B vitamins. They yield the vitamins in large numbers, but not in sufficient amounts to make any significant differences unless one takes prohibitively large quantities. If one eats an ordinary diet, *even a poor diet,* he gets some of *every known vitamin* (this can hardly be avoided); the important question is: Does he get *enough* of each? In my book *Nutrition and Alcoholism,* this subject is discussed more fully and more specific information is given.

If amino acid deficiencies are responsible for some difficulty in one's bodily machinery, then about the only practical way to meet this situation is to eat an abundance of good protein food—meat, cheese, etc. If one is a millionaire, he might be able to buy enough pure amino acids. Here again it is the *quantity* of each which is important, not the number of amino acids included.

As set forth more fully in the book referred to above, there is a real hope that many diseases aside from alcoholism, including some of those classified as "mental," may be attacked nutritionally with some degree of success *if the distinctiveness of individual needs is recognized.*

These attacks to be even partially successful must be made by individuals who are thoroughly conversant with the fundamental biochemistry involved. They will not involve such expedients as the substitution of eggs for cheese, of bananas for apricots, but rather the administration of suitable amounts of known nutrients and metabolites, which may, with some reasonable hope, be expected to correct specific deficiencies. In this type of investigation one is not limited to the use of substances which are known to be needed by all people; there may be useful metabolites which are usually not required, but which, for specific reasons, are needed in individual cases.

Every individual should during youth be fed highly diversified food according to the well-developed principles of good nutrition, but no hidebound formula can apply. If in spite of this difficulties arise, there should be adequate investigations and trials made to determine whether special nutritional deficiencies (occasioned by an inherited large demand) may be responsible for the trouble.

If during adult years an individual gets along without difficulties of a nutritional nature (including those which may have a nutritional origin), well and good. If not, a serious attempt should be made to correct deficiencies which appear in later life. As our metabolic machinery ages, special demands may arise which are not observed during earlier years. Each of us inherits not only his basic metabolic machinery but also a characteristic pattern of aging. In every case an intelligent approach must include a recognition of inborn variability.

XI

The Fallacy of "The Patient"

THE PRECLINICAL education of physicians, like the education of all other citizens, is largely based upon the tacit concept that people are either "normal" or else they are "defective." Eighteen years of education along this line is enough to ground most of the embryonic doctors pretty thoroughly in the idea.

In spite of this, premedical students do learn something of variability in the biological kingdom as applied to plants and animals, and the importance of the phenomenon in connection with human beings is not denied—except through the implied denial inherent in the failure to emphasize. This failure to emphasize betokens an unusual and paradoxical attitude of mind which is widespread. Scholars in the field are quite aware of the fact that variability is a *sine qua non* of evolution, and that it is certainly applicable to human beings—and yet they continue to oversimplify and distort the human picture by leaving variability out just when its inclusion would make a world of difference.

Without doubt, in routine teaching it is felt that the idea of human variability would so complicate the picture for immature students that excluding it seems often the better policy. Because of the importance of variability, however, this does not absolve the biology teacher from his responsibility. Another and possibly more important consideration bearing on the neglect of human variability is related to the status of biology as a science. Sciences do and must deal in generalizations, and the more fully developed they are the more exact and far reaching are the laws which apply. Biology in seeking to become a science has felt the urge to generalize and sometimes there has been a temptation to allow spurious and premature generalizations to take root in lieu of more valid ones. The fact of human variability is an obstruction—an enemy—standing in the way of generalization, and hence may be regarded as the enemy of "scientific" biology. For this reason it may often be considered an unwelcome guest.

We can generalize about human beings with respect to certain attributes, but, because of extreme variability, we have to be very careful how widely we range in our generalizations if we wish to remain within the bounds of truth. As soon as we generalize completely and talk and think exclusively about *"man,"* we blind ourselves to the numerous problems that arise directly and indirectly out of variability.

I can cite a number of otherwise excellent books (among the best there are) on physiology, pharmacology, biochemistry, physiological psychology, and related fields which give no hint as to the possible importance of inborn human variability in connection with the respective fields. *The human body* (in effect a denial or an ignoring of variability) is, in these volumes, the beginning, the middle, and the end. The physiological, pharmacological, biochemical, and physio-psychological variations (which can be demonstrated to be tremendous) are mentioned, if at all, in an offhand manner as if they were of very minor or passing interest. Items of variability are likely to be treated as "flies in the ointment"—at best, exceptions which tend to prove the rule, or at worst, unfortunate obstacles which actually stand in the way of generalization.

It is admittedly true that each of the subjects listed above becomes much more complicated the moment we admit the consideration of wide human variability. Shall we therefore accept the simple and untrue in preference to the complicated and true? Much of the subject matter of biology would be simpler and easier to systematize, if variability did not exist. However, evolution could not have happened. Physiology and psychology as subjects for study would be vastly simpler if it were not for variability. But we are living in a fool's paradise as long as we leave human variability out of our thinking.

When a prospective physician completes his more formal education and is ready to begin dealing with real cases in the clinics, his mental approach is understandably pretty well set, and he often continues to think of exceptions as unfortunate incidents (refractory cases). But sometimes his mental make-up and his associations will fortunately emancipate him from excessive domination by the idea of normality.

I was told by a surgeon that one of the most striking facts he had learned through practical experience (not in medical school) was that when two people have substantially the same injury, one may hardly notice it while the other may be completely disabled by the pain. He came to recognize this difference as due to biological variability.

This sort of fact, and the insight which goes with it, should certainly not need to be learned by *experience*. Every physician should gain such insight as a part of his basic training. It is well known that a few people are insensitive to pain; they simply do not have the neurological machinery that allows them to feel it. If we merely throw such people out of consideration saying they are "abnormal" (not satisfactory assembly-line products), we have learned nothing from them. If we realize that they represent extreme cases, that all gradations of sensitivity to pain are to be expected, we have learned an important fact about people. Aside from wide variability in general sensitivity to pain, there is probably additional variation with respect to the sensitivity of specific body areas. What physicians sometimes dismiss lightly as "psychic pain" (the kind that supposedly originates in one's mind) may often be found to be attributable to hypersensitivity. The absence of a lesion which is *apparently sufficient* to cause the observed pain does not rule out the existence of an undetected lesion which may actually be sufficient—a specific sensitivity of the individual.

Numerous cases have come to my attention in which physicians have, greatly to their patients' discomfort, insisted on using certain anesthetics and drugs in spite of the fact that they had been warned in advance of their unusual effects on the individual concerned. In these cases it seemed that the physicians were determined willy-nilly that their patients shall be normal assembly-line products. Incidents like these, of which I have direct knowledge, have involved older physicians. It is to be hoped that physicians now completing their training know better.

In spite of the fact that physicians are required in their premedical training to learn something about genetics and heredity, these are subjects which come up relatively rarely and reluctantly in their thinking, and which are seldom applied. While experts in the field are thoroughly convinced that susceptibility to numerous specific diseases is inherited, physicians hesitate to mention this fact to their patients or to admit it even to themselves. It is understandable that in relation to a patient they should take this attitude: "I can do nothing about changing your ancestors; *you* are here before me; let's see what can be done for you. We will not mention or even consider your unchangeable inheritance."

The fallacy of this well-meaning point of view is that, while possibly the patient need not be told, it seems altogether probable that if the physician does not know or will not consider the real nature of the trouble, he will be far less helpful than he should be. Actually people carry their heredity with them, in every cell of their bodies, and it is with this bundle of heredity that the physician has to work. On the basis of the biological point of view which we have developed, hereditary factors probably enter into every tendency to contract or resist disease.

Nowhere has the assembly-line doctrine, or a close approximation to it, taken firmer hold than in certain fields of psychiatry. Essentially the approach is this: When people have mental troubles, there must be a reason for it; let us search back into the earlier psychological experiences and bring the causes out into the open. This in itself is an admirable idea and often brings effective help.

The severe limitation to this approach is that it tacitly makes the assumption that all babies at the start are the same. It fails to consider what seems biologically to be undeniable, that each baby has a set of blank pages or potentialities which are distinct for that baby as distinguished from any other and that these are extremely important in determining how his mental processes will function in future years. The evidence that the tendency toward schizophrenia is inherited is in line with what one would expect on the biological basis.

The extreme emphasis on the importance of environmental influences has led to some searchings which seem absurd. If a psychoanalyst can find nothing in the recent history of an individual which will account for the difficulty, he goes back further and further in search of something. Some, I understand, pursue the matter back to prenatal environment and supposed prenatal psychic experience—neglecting all the time the biological concept that each developing egg cell of human origin is endowed by inheritance not only with human potentialities but with a distinctive pattern of intellectual potentialities.

This exclusively environmental approach also throws a terrific burden on those who have the responsibility of caring for children. It is well known that children's physical bodies can stand all sorts of wounds and mutilations—that their power for complete recovery is great. But mentally, it is assumed, with far from adequate proof, that they can be seriously wounded by some trivial neglect or by some temporary allegedly improper treatment. Certainly the extent to which psychic trauma in early years can cause permanent damage is unknown, and there is no hope of finding out until the facts of biological variability are taken into account. In the meantime it is shameful that many children have been alienated from their parents because of the poorly supported supposition that their early treatment has been devastating in its effect.

That there is often a close connection between mental difficulties and sex is generally recognized even by those who do not accept Freudian concepts. Many who have thought of biological variability as being merely academically interesting should have had their eyes opened by a consideration of some of the facts detailed in the Kinsey report. The almost unbelievable variation of forty thousand fold has already been mentioned. Surely one would have to be uninitiated in the realm of glandular anatomy and physiology to suppose that such differences are primarily of environmental origin. It seems hopeless to try to understand the intimate relationships which probably exist between sex and mental disease without taking into account the tremendous magnitude of sex variation.

In the so-called psychosomatic approach to medicine the mind-body relationships which are more often stressed are those in which mental attitudes affect bodily functioning. Actually, of course, the relationships are two-way; many times mental attitudes are greatly affected by bodily conditions. The administration of the hormone cortisone, to cite a single example, often produces a marked exhilaration, optimism, and sense of well-being. The responsibility for finding the seat of the difficulty in obscure maladies should not be shirked by those equipped to investigate the physiological origins. It may be disastrous to pass the buck to those who may blame the difficulty on the mental state.

Actually while the recognition of wide human variability has the effect of making physiology and psychology more difficult branches of science, it may clarify or simplify tremendously many specific problems in which variability is intimately involved. One of these problems is that of alcoholism.

Up until a few years ago alcoholism was looked upon as purely an environmental matter. It was supposed that alcohol did "something" to "the human body" and as a result the individual became an alcoholic. Volumes were written on the subject; practically all writers accepted tacitly the ideas that everyone starts "even," so to speak, and that differences in reactions and responses to alcohol on the part of individuals was accidental. Many sought to find in the cultures of peoples the reason for their peculiarities in behavior with respect to alcohol. A number of extensive studies were made of more or less primitive tribes and their experience with alcohol, all completely disregarding, without even a bare mention, the possibility that inborn differences might exist. It had long been observed, for instance, that Jewish people seldom were alcoholics. Instead of considering the possibility that inheritance might play a role here as it does in the higher incidence of diabetes among Jewish people, at least one extensive study was made purporting to show that cultural differences were responsible for the decreased incidence of alcoholism among Jews, without even mentioning that inheritance *might* be involved. The acceptance as axiomatic of this point of view is hard to justify, because the Jewish culture is a religious one, from which many people of Jewish descent have now departed. Furthermore the Jewish culture itself grew out of the Jewish people who had a unique biological background.

As a result of all the deliberations and investigations relating to alcoholism (most of which involved uncritical acceptance of the assembly-line doctrine) the problem remained an unsolved one. While certain measures such as the "aversion" therapy seemed to be of some benefit, and Alcoholics Anonymous did a marvelous work in salvaging numerous individuals by a religious and gregarious approach, the causes of alcoholism remained obscure; any really successful medical treatment was not available, and physicians and hospitals very often refused alcoholic patients.

Shortly after the writer's book *The Human Frontier* was published, it was determined that an approach to the investigation of alcoholism would be made *on the assumption that inborn differences might be important.* In other words we rejected the assembly-line doctrine and adopted the only view which could really be considered biologically acceptable.

In a surprisingly short time after the problem of alcoholism was attacked from this new point of view the light began to break, and my colleagues and I began to see what we believe to be both a reason for the disease and a way to cure and prevent it.

Our initial illuminating observations were made with experimental animals. These we put into individual cages and watched individually, deliberately avoiding striking any averages. The rats, on an ordinary stock diet, were each given access to two drinking bottles, one containing water and the other a 10 per cent alcohol solution. The positions of the two bottles were switched daily and, by recording the consumption from each bottle, we determined the drinking tendencies of the individual rats.

That each of the individual rats in a colony such as ours had its own inherited differences became apparent as we began charting the alcoholic consumption. Some rats consumed alcohol rather heavily the first time it was offered and continuously thereafter. At the other extreme were some rats which never consumed any alcohol although each was forced to make a deliberate choice. Intermediate were rats which drank very moderately throughout, and many which drank a little at first and progressively more after a few weeks or after a longer period.

Not only did it become clear, by experiments involving rats with different genetic backgrounds, that inheritance was involved in the tendency of the rats to drink, but it became apparent that diet was an important factor also. When the drinking rats in our original colony had their diets supplemented with certain vitamins, they stopped drinking overnight; when these rats were placed on poor diets, marginal with respect to certain vitamins, they all drank alcohol rather heavily; when they were placed on abundant diets, none of the rats drank!

When our experiments were extended to rats from other colonies having different genetic backgrounds, the results were somewhat different in that our "abundant diets" were not good enough for all the rats. Many could be prevented from drinking, or cured of drinking, but by no means all, and it is evident that there are still unknown vitamin-like substances which will have to be introduced into the diets in sufficient quantities before *all* rats can be successfully treated.

While we were not naive enough to suppose that all the factors that enter into alcoholism would be observable in rats, human experiments have followed the same pattern, as has been set forth in the writer's book *Nutrition and Alcoholism*, and it seems increasingly clear that certain individuals are susceptible to alcoholism because they have inborn nutritional demands which are unusually high, and for this reason they are susceptible to deficiencies that others escape. When these individuals have their nutritional deficiencies continuously taken care of, they are no different from their nonalcoholic friends, so far as alcohol consumption is concerned.

Unfortunately, however, as far as the experiments of others as well as of ourselves have gone, human beings respond too much like the rats: By no means all are "cured" by the available nutritional treatment. In fact the proportion of human beings who are greatly benefited may be smaller than that of experimental rats taken at random. Nevertheless a substantial percentage of those who have taken nutritional supplements continuously have been transformed almost miraculously into individuals who have no alcohol problem.

There are numerous factors which make it extremely difficult to get reliable information regarding substantial numbers of alcoholics. For one thing alcoholism has been considered a psychiatric problem and most psychiatrists are not receptive to innovations which run counter to their basic concepts. For this reason it is difficult to get a nutritional treatment tried out in a systematic manner. It is essential, of course, that the person under treatment take the prescribed nutritional supplements consistently. People in general will not take capsules unless they think they have something wrong with them that the capsules are likely to help. If the physician in charge has no confidence in the treatment he is administering, patients are likely not to take it. Often patients do not cooperate anyway. Probably many of those alcoholics who have seemingly failed to respond to nutritional supplements have really not taken them as they were supposed to have done.

Since animal experiments have indicated the existence of unknown nutrients which are effective in preventing alcoholic consumption, and since these "unknowns" are being investigated both in this country and abroad, there is a strong hope that the nutritional approach to alcoholism will eventually be highly successful. By accepting inborn variability as a scientific fact, the problem of alcoholism has been solved for some individuals and the way has been pointed toward its solution for others.

There is excellent reason for thinking that many medical and other problems will be clarified and simplified when they are attacked not from the standpoint of that mythical hunk of humanity "the patient," but with the full recognition that inborn differences of *each* patient may be important. The nutritional approach alone has great potentialities when it is made with this point of view.

The idea that people vary widely in their nutritional needs, that is, in the *quantities* of the different nutrients needed, is a crucial one from the standpoint of our present discussion. Because it has not been fashionable to study individuals, very little reliable information involving numbers of individuals is available on this point. The needs for thiamin have been investigated in sixteen individuals and in this small group there was apparently a four-fold range in the needs. If the group had been much larger, the range would doubtless have been considerably greater.

I know a scientist of excellent repute who discovered somewhat accidentally that he had an unusual demand for ascorbic acid (vitamin C). He had great difficulty with his teeth and gums and had to see a dentist at very short intervals, but without material relief. When large doses of ascorbic acid were taken or, better yet, when quantities of citrus juice were consumed daily, the difficulty completely disappeared; he remains well in this respect as long as he continues the nutritional supplement. Interestingly, his son has the same difficulty and his condition is held in check by the same means.

Another prominent scientist was afflicted by psoriasis, a skin disease of obscure origin. He discovered that taking large doses of vitamin A continuously (about ten times what is supposed to be the usual need) caused his psoriasis to disappear. When he was in a foreign country and ran out of the vitamin supply, the disease reappeared. He returned to this country but decided to neglect the supplement for a time. The condition got worse, however, so he began taking the extra vitamin A again, and the psoriasis disappeared as before.

Another well-trained scientist was afflicted with such severe headaches that he was almost incapacitated. Taking a vitamin mixture helped greatly, and he went to the trouble to find out by blind trials, with the cooperation of a pharmacist, what ingredient was responsible. It turned out to be thiamin. When he took plenty of extra thiamin, his difficulty vanished.

It is interesting that all sorts of miscellaneous benefits have been reported (and with considerable consistency in some cases) from the taking of the nutritional supplement containing an abundance of a wide assortment of nutritional factors which we have devised for alcoholics. Insomnia has often appeared to have been greatly benefited; hypertension, headaches, and allergies have yielded in specific cases. All of these facts, coupled with the complete validity of the principle from the genetic standpoint, make it seem certain that the individual variability in nutritional needs is large and that many diseases may yield when attacked with this in mind.

That inborn differences, detectable by biochemical means, are important considerations in connection with other diseases, including those in which minds are involved, is indicated by further researches carried on at the University of Texas.

Our study of individual human beings has revealed that each person has a distinctive metabolic pattern and that these patterns are significant not only in connection with the problem of alcoholism but also in obesity, schizophrenia, and mental deficiency.

The patterns of twelve different individuals are graphically exemplified in twelve charts appearing on pages 108 and 109. Each radiating line in the graphs represents by its length a measurable item in the person's pattern.* In order to plot these items, it was necessary to adopt a scale, and the scale chosen was based upon the average values for each item measured.

Close inspection shows that each figure is a highly distinctive one, but that numbers 11 and 12 are more similar than any other two. These two

* The successive numbered lines represent items as follows: 1–5, taste sensitivities for creatinine, sugar, potassium chloride, sodium chloride, hydrochloric acid; 6–17, salivary constituents—uric acid, glucose, leucine, valine, citrulline, alanine, lysine, taurine, glycine, serine, glutamic acid, aspartic acid; 18–31, urinary constituents—citrate, unknown base Rf .28, unknown acid Rf .32, gonadotropic hormone (pituitary), pH, pigment/creatinine ratio, chloride/creatinine ratio, hippuric/creatinine ratio, creatinine, taurine, glycine, serine, citrulline, alanine.

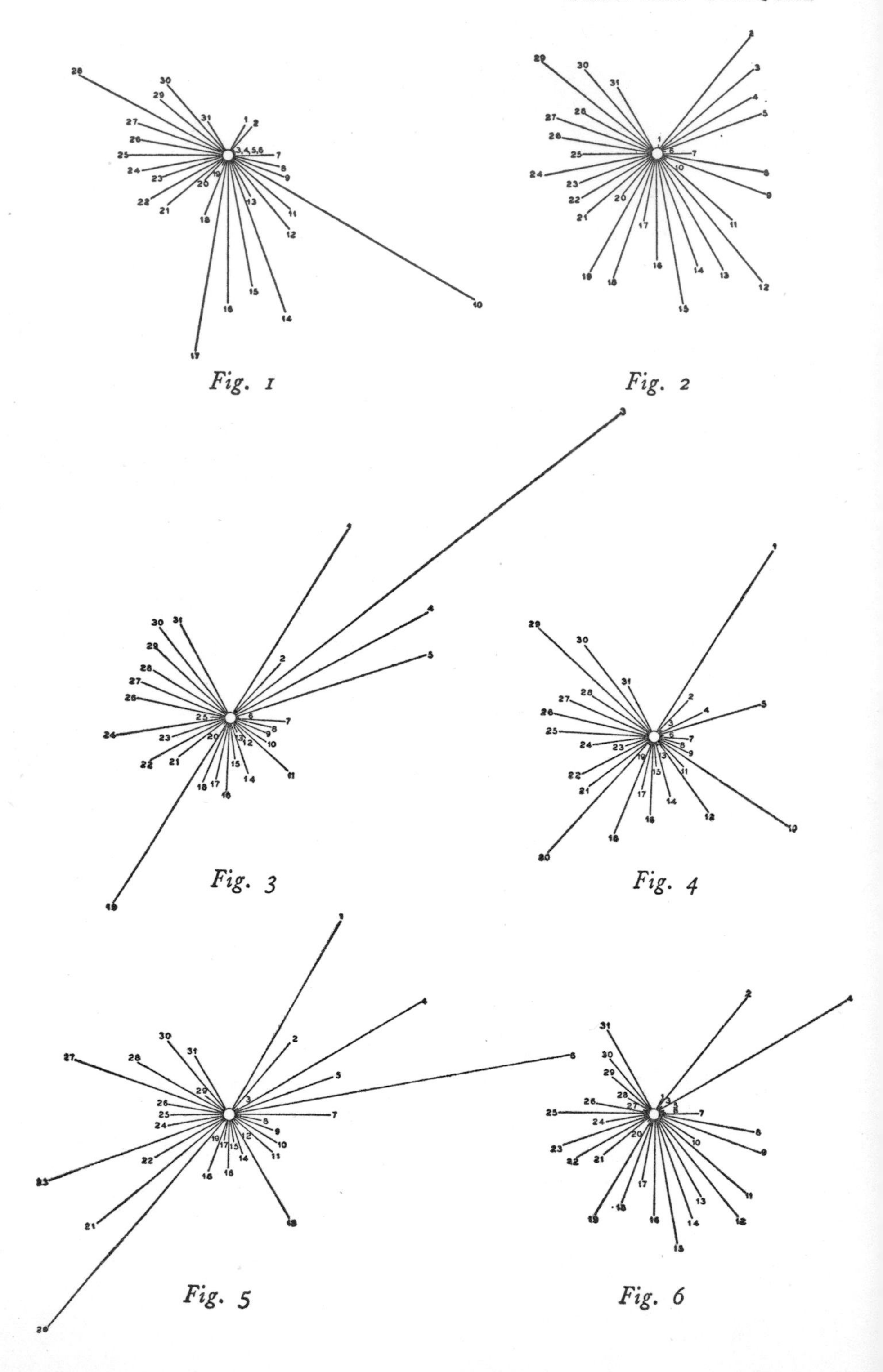

Fig. 1

Fig. 2

Fig. 3

Fig. 4

Fig. 5

Fig. 6

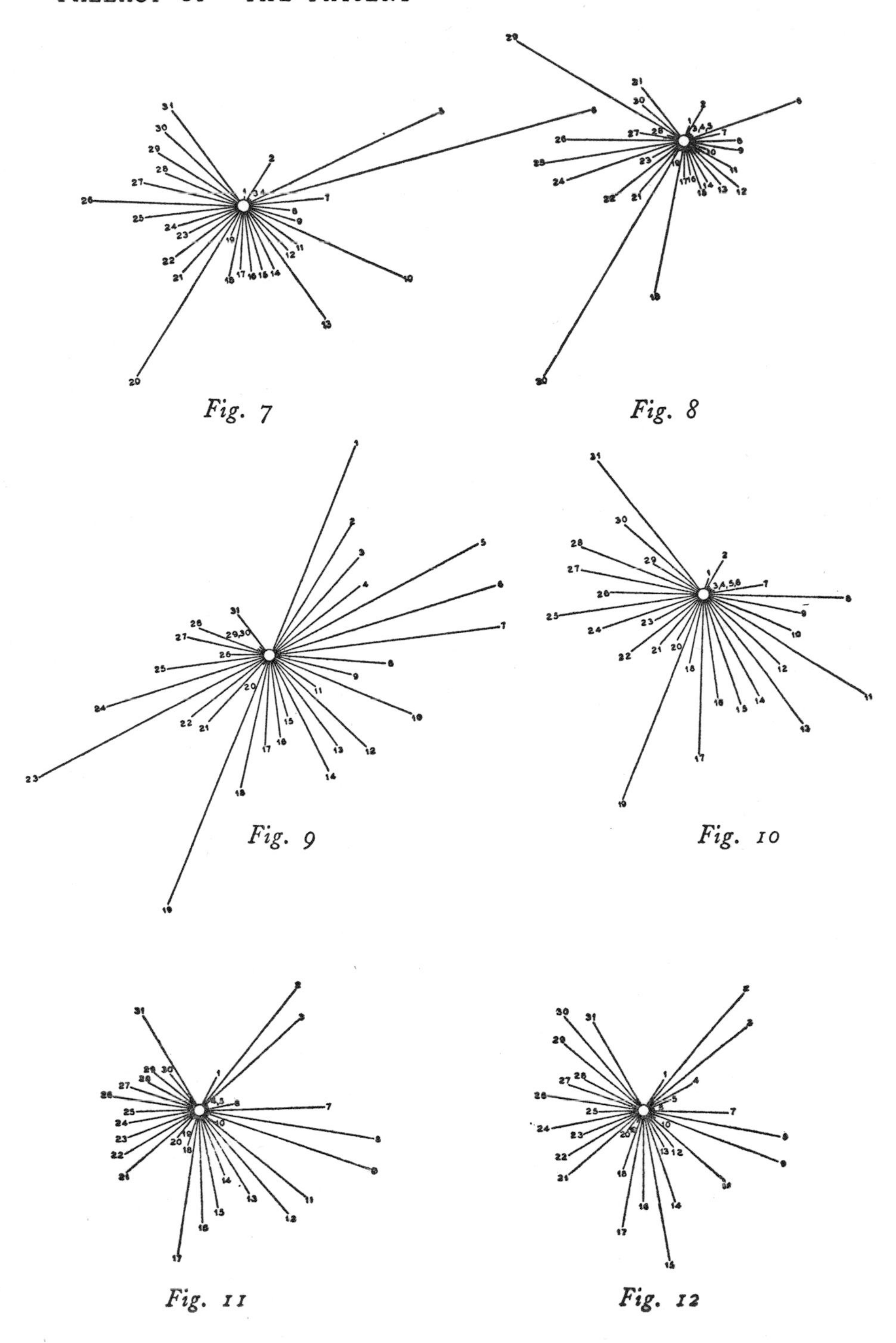

Fig. 7

Fig. 8

Fig. 9

Fig. 10

Fig. 11

Fig. 12

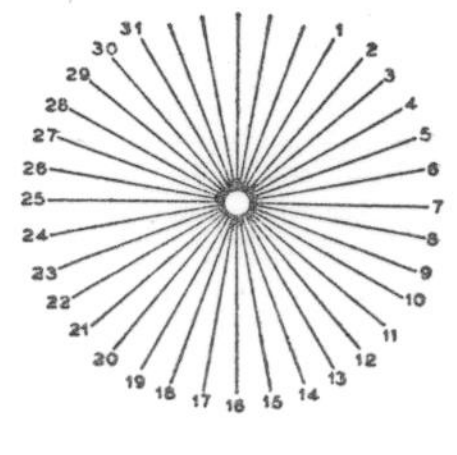

Fig. 13

patterns belong to so-called "identical" twins, indicating that heredity has much to do with these patterns.

As has already been mentioned, these patterns are significant with respect to various problems—alcoholism, obesity, mental disease, and mental deficiency—as demonstrated by the fact that statistical differences in patterns appear when the different groups are compared: alcoholics *vs.* nonalcoholics, obese *vs.* nonobese, etc. One reason for presenting them at this point is to call attention to their distinctiveness and to the fact that if we average all these patterns together, we get Figure 13, above, which is the graph for a hypothetical average individual. By averaging, as we indicated earlier, we abolish all the patterns. The same principle was involved in our experiments with rats earlier described. If we had averaged together the alcohol consumption curves of the rats originally observed, we would have destroyed all their individual patterns, and come out with a result which resembled the pattern of not a single rat.

Progress in the field of medicine as well as in other fields demands full and constant awareness of the facts of human variability and an abandonment of the "normality" doctrine which has blinded us in our attempts to solve many human problems. "The patient" is only the roughest approximation. To be most effective, physicians must know a great deal about individuality and must treat distinctive individuals each with his inborn differences.

About the time that the first draft of this book was completed, I lost my life companion (to whose memory this book is dedicated) under circumstances which made me realize more than ever before how important the study of individual differences can be in the field of medicine. When medical deficiencies strike at one's own home, the blow cannot be brushed aside. As I become able to overcome the emotional shock of the loss and the tragedy of her illness, I resolve to do what I can to forward more pointedly than ever the type of investigations that will, I believe, help prevent such calamities.

She had lived a full, highly influential, and for the most part happy life, of which I am proud. It might have continued to its full span if her emotional life had not been upset by the menopause and particularly by the wreckage resulting from the radium sterilization which she underwent at the hands of physicians who may have known how to treat "the menopause patient," but did not know how to treat her. During her lifetime I always stoutly defended the physicians concerned, because I realized that they were acting according to accepted principles, and furthermore I knew that bitterness on her part could only make matters worse. In spite of anything I could do or say bitterness persisted, though she rarely devoted attention to it.

It is perfectly obvious to me that her periods of extreme depression were due to hormonal imbalance, because scores of times she was brought out of these periods by the expedient of hormone administration, and the world became very rosy indeed. The effects were so dramatic and were repeated so many times that there is no doubt in my mind as to the seat of her difficulty.

No physician whom I ever encountered or whom she ever consulted would have denied for an instant that she was an individual and as such needed individual attention. What all of them lacked (and the lack was serious) was substantial knowledge of *how she differed* from other individuals, or any serious interest in finding out how she differed, or any significant appreciation of how such information might help. Some doctors disbelieved in the administration of hormones under any circumstances on the grounds that "the human body will adjust"; others had great faith in stilbesterol; others warned against it and used natural estrone; others tried testosterone. Some advocated injections only, others not. None seemed to have adequate appreciation of the probability that her needs may have been peculiarly different from those of other patients. The fact that different doctors had diverse opinions was not in itself alarming; the fact that they appeared so often to be both unintelligent and dogmatic was disturbing.

I am aware of the intricacies of hormone therapy and it is obvious to anyone familiar with the field that, even if an individual physician had sought to find the answer on an individual basis, he might easily have failed because of lack of background information. What is needed is vastly more attention by research scientists and physicians—over a period of years—to the problem of how so-called normal individuals vary in their hormonal patterns. I do affirm, with all the earnestness I can command, that *individuals and their differences must be studied* before such tragedies as happened in my family can be prevented. This is something which I ardently hope physicians generally will come to appreciate.

XII

Religious and Artistic Fits and Misfits

IN THE FIELD of religion, that almost universal experience, abundant illustrations can be found of the fact that diversity of human thinking and human wanting has played an exceedingly important role, and that inborn human characteristics have been too little recognized. The same may be said of art, which in its broadest concept is akin to religion.

Without posing as a historian, theologian, or art critic, I wish to point out, even if in a cursory way, some of the implications as I see them. It is my hope that others who are experts in these fields will see more than I do, and that the biological facts regarding human nature and individuality will eventually be integrated into a more satisfactory interpretation of religion and art than has hitherto been possible.

I cannot speak with any degree of familiarity about the founders of other religions, but I do think it is clear that Jesus exhibited a profound appreciation of the individuality of his disciples and others. His emphatic admonition, "Judge not," might almost be used to designate the theme of this book. Jesus' appreciation of the diverse ways of Mary and Martha was a demonstration that he practiced what he preached. The parable of the talents was in accord with the same theme. When he said,

"In my Father's house are many mansions," the import of individuality was stressed, as it was also when God's care, not only for individual human beings but even for sparrows, was expounded. The parable of the lost sheep and the ninety and nine in the fold bespeaks an interest in individual people quite out of line with the uniformity doctrine. In fact, the whole tone of Jesus' life as set forth in the New Testament was that of appreciation of individual worth.

Not long ago I read a well-intentioned article expounding the theme that Jesus' apostles were like clay in the Master's hands, and that they became great men as an exemplification of the principle that under his touch something came out of nothing. I do not believe that scholars in the field agree even remotely that this is so. Every New Testament writer approached his subject from a different angle; certainly there was no lack of individuality in the disciples even when the training period was over.

The avowed followers of Christianity have exhibited throughout history a remarkable assortment of inclinations and disinclinations (for example, from extreme authoritarianism to extreme freedom and lack of organization), a fact which to my mind bespeaks a diversity of mental patterns and a tendency of these patterns to resist being revolutionized by training.

In our American history we find religious liberty playing an important role. We have traditionally affirmed the right of every individual to follow his own conscience—something that we would not care about if we were all alike.

Actually, however, we have by no means lived up to our high ideals. The Puritans had a strong urge to force their Puritanism on others, and they have not been alone in this fault. As it seems to me, human beings have always exhibited too strong a tendency to judge others by themselves. Parents generally have a desire that their children, even when they grow up, should follow a course which they, the parents, could justify and approve for themselves. Children are very often put in an embarrassing position unless they accept the religious ideas and practices of mother or father. A general recognition of the diverse patterns of personality and of mental make-up should go a long way toward promoting real religious liberty—the kind that would permit each individual to follow his own religious leanings without stress or embarrassment.

Of course history tells us all too vividly of the cruelty of the religious battles of the past, in which followers of religion have tried to force their ideas upon others.

It does not appear to me, however, that Jesus' teaching—or any sound teaching—suggests that people should not pass value judgments or should make no attempt to discriminate between right and wrong. "Judge not" means to me that one should avoid jumping to conclusions regarding what is unknown—the innermost motives of other individuals—and should be generous enough to make allowances for differences in personality.

For people to live healthily and happily seems to require that they be adjusted not only to their outward environment but to their inner natures. If there is a moral urge which resides in all of us and is a part of human nature, then a neglect or avoidance of this urge can mean serious maladjustment.

The idea that individuals are born like similar lumps of putty to be molded by nurture and training carries with it the implication that there is no basic morality or urge to do right, and that all the morality we have is that which is trained into us. Conditioned reflexes are all that is involved, and morality is merely habit and custom. Being moral, then, according to this concept, merely means following the prevailing customs. Conscience then becomes merely an urge to conform to custom.

While we have stressed as fundamental to the theme of this book the need for understanding human differences, this does not mean a denial of a common core of likenesses. One of the ways in which we human beings are born alike, so it seems to me, is in the possession of a moral capacity—a capacity to desire right in preference to wrong in the same sense that we have a capacity to appreciate the unchanging verity of the concept that two plus two equals four. For this reason we may be said to be "made in the image of God." It is true, no doubt, that people differ in their keenness of moral sense, just as they do in keenness of arithmetical sense, yet there would appear to be some justification in regarding a hypothetical being who has *no* moral sense as subhuman.

The idea that morality is wholly a matter of training and that there is no fundamental moral urge common to humanity is quite contrary to the ideas of our forefathers who established this nation. If, in opposition to the older view, training is everything and originality is to be encouraged, the one who feels constrained to initiate changes in customs *and morals* is not doing wrong; he is merely running the risk of incurring disfavor at the hands of his fellows and should not be criticized.

There is serious question as to whether the whole moral fiber of our country has not been severely damaged by the application of this philosophy, and whether the exalted and exaggerated position in which we have placed training is not responsible. Have we not come to think of morality as being elastic and subject to modification by training? If a candidate for public office promises to be economical, is elected, and later decides to be profligate, he need make no explanation or apology; political promises are not made to be kept. If a person traveling at company expense pads his expense account, it is not wrong. Custom expects one to do this. If a government official asks for more money for his department than he needs (or expects to get) or builds up or perpetuates a staff unnecessarily or duplicates the work of others, this is according to custom and hence is morally right. However, because we have not yet quite arrived at the point where it is a generalized custom for a government employee to accept presents and at the same time use influence to aid the giver, we hedge on whether or not it is moral.

A more old-fashioned view of such goings on as we have described is that they are all morally wrong. The man who makes campaign promises he doesn't expect to try to keep is guilty of *lying*. The person who obtains money or goods falsely is guilty of *stealing*, and one who builds up bureaucratic organization without justification is nonetheless a thief, because he is stealing from the public.

One of the tragedies of war is the moral tragedy. In war we forget our morals. Lying, stealing, and killing, which we commonly regard as wrong, become the order of the day, and it would not be a war with these left out. The more often we lapse into war, the more likely we are to lose all morality. But I believe that, on the whole, people individually do not want war; they find themselves enmeshed and know no way to avoid it. (The ignoring of human variability, in fact, has a great deal to do with their being enmeshed.) One of the encouraging signs of an advancing morality is the fact that so many people *hate* war. It seems that a certain desire for morality is part of the fundamental make-up of all of us; and I do not believe that, built as we are, we will ever abandon our desire for it. Hunger and thirst after righteousness are real and enduringly strong.

Almost equally strong is the desire for beauty and its creative expression. The environmentalist who wishes to retain his point of view—that what one is depends essentially upon his training—should not look too carefully at the field of artistic creation. If we are born essentially alike, how did the creative artists of all ages arise? What do you have to feed babies or how do you have to treat them to get them to turn out to be a Mozart, a Rembrandt, or a Shakespeare? I suppose it is belaboring the obvious to insist that the inheritance of these individuals must have had a great deal to do with their superlative performance.

How about you and me and our neighbors? Do hereditary factors enter into our enjoyment of art and if so what misfits and misunderstandings are caused by our differences? One of the reasons why I feel certain that inborn differences come prominently into play is that I see in myself, in members of my family, and in friends, artistic inclinations and disinclinations that in my judgment could not possibly have been produced by training.

For many years I have derived keen enjoyment from certain types of art, particularly those involving form in contrast to those involving color. I still have keen remembrance of the thrills I experienced on several occasions many years ago—when at the Chicago Art Institute I was exhilarated by statues of Joan of Arc and Voltaire, when I was confronted unexpectedly by superb architecture on the Yale University campus, and when I saw the wonderful strength in the face of the Venus de Milo in the Louvre. The pictures that have made the greatest impression on me are those in which form predominates. It is not that I am indifferent to color, but I do not have the same keen feeling for it that I have for form. I feel very sure that this feeling comes *out of me* and that it did not arise as a result of peculiarities in my education.

Of course, the mass of material which has already been set forth in earlier chapters of this book, including the material on "signatures," has influenced my thinking with respect to art. A specific finding, in addition to the experiences already cited, has made me more certain than ever that leanings in art are to a considerable extent inborn.

Maitland Graves in his book *The Art of Color and Design* has set up a series of twenty pairs of designs (purposely made not to look like any specific physical objects that might have determinative associations) from which one may choose, in each of the twenty cases, the better and more pleasing design of the two. Without reading his discussion of design or having any previous training whatever, I was able to pick with certainty the "right" design in every case. Why could I do this and why do other individuals often react very differently? Some, according to Graves, are almost as likely to pick the wrong design as the right one, and such individuals are of course not encouraged to study for a career in the field of design. There seems to be no question that there is great diversity in the native abilities of different individuals to discriminate with respect to design and to appreciate what is commonly regarded as excellent.

With respect to music a similar situation exists, in that I find in myself a pattern of likes and abilities and interests that are characteristic of me. Since this is not a biographical sketch, I will not detail these. It is perhaps sufficient to say that as we have earlier indicated there are many facets to musical ability, and I find myself unusually strong in some and weak in others, just as Seashore sometimes found for professional musicians. These differences are not directly related to my training, since I have had the most training in the areas where I am weakest.

It seems important for people to realize that in the field of art, as in religion, there are inborn differences which play an important role. We should not ignorantly try to impose our artistic tastes on others, nor imagine that everyone is perfectly adaptable in these matters. I recently talked to a professional musician who apparently had no appreciation for what I believe to be the facts in the case. When I indicated a lack of enthusiasm for a new composition—it was modern music and had just been played in public for the first time—he indicated to me quite emphatically (not even having heard the piece, himself) that it was merely because of my inexperience; if I would listen to it repeatedly and get acquainted with it, I would like it as well as anyone. Actually some examples of modern music interest and attract me easily, and I cannot believe that my appreciation of music rests wholly on repetitive hearing or on my being told that it is beautiful.

Inborn differences enter, I believe, into the attitudes which people take toward various types of modern art. This does not deny that training is highly important also. For people who have an assortment of artistic leanings that makes design and color of primary interest and subject matter secondary, a modern painting which "looks like nothing" may be excellent. The proof of the pudding is in the eating, and if certain people enjoy a work of art, that is justification for its existence. Originality in art is certainly to be commended, and any work which is original, and at the same time interesting and attractive to a substantial number of people, is a contribution in a sense that a picture lacking originality cannot be.

One of the most important gains to be achieved in the field of art as a result of rejecting the uniformity doctrine is better understanding and better relations between artists and between appreciators of art. If we think everyone is uncouth who has different artistic tastes from ours or who lacks taste along lines in which we are superior, we are not only judging, we are misjudging. A tremendous amount of needless human friction arises out of such an attitude when it is applied in the various fields of art, including music and literature. Because I personally feel a strong attraction to works of sculpture, I should not laugh at a neighbor who has no appreciation in this area. I realize that many of these capacities are inborn and my neighbor probably has other capacities which I lack.

Artists often do not get along well with other artists, and musicians often depreciate their fellow musicians. Why? Because artists and musicians often have strong positive tastes and, like all the rest of us, they tend to judge others, using themselves as the yardstick. They may be quite honest in believing that their own work is superior and that of their fellows is inferior. The best they can do is to be polite and pretend to be agreeable.

The strong urges which human beings have for religion, morality, and beauty are potent evidences for the unity (and Divine origin, if you will) of the human race. The fact that a tremendous multiplicity of forms of expression arises from these urges is proof of the strongest sort that men are highly variable. Human beings have been described as religious animals, but the expressions of religion have been multitudinous and diverse beyond description. A high regard for beauty is well nigh universal, but the expressions which it takes in paintings, sculptures, music, dancing, in poetry, drama, and all forms of literature are almost as diverse as life itself.

To understand the roots of these divergences is to gain in the understanding of human nature. We have differences which need to be understood, and likenesses which make us want to understand.

XIII

Races, Peoples, Individuality

IN THE AREA of race relations we emphatically need "more light and less heat." Throughout our history, the relationships between white Americans and people of other racial origins have been distressingly bad. Our record with respect to the American Indians up to the present time is about as far removed from our professed ideals as can be imagined. As we all know, slavery created the Negro problem. Our attitudes toward Oriental people, Chinese and others, and our treatment of them, cannot be a matter of great pride.

Any insight into human nature which we can gain should help us understand why we behave as we do. Biological variability is undoubtedly one of the factors in the complex situation, and we will briefly outline some of the implications which appear most obvious from this standpoint.

In the first place the term *race* is often badly used and at best has an indefinite meaning. Experts cannot agree as to how many races there are or how many sub-races, because of the complexity of interbreeding and the fact that such a large proportion of human beings have mixed racial origins.

However, from the biological point of view, it is now clear how ethnic groups originate. Whenever a segment of the population becomes separated and lives in a more or less isolated region for a number of generations, it develops a group with a set of inheritances that is characteristic of that group. If the isolation is complete and lasts for a long time, the isolated population becomes more homogeneous (in spite of biological variation which diminishes but remains great) and there are increasing chances for mutations to become incorporated which will make the group more and more distinctive and different. Geneticists have good reasons for thinking that mutations are taking place all of the time in all kinds of populations.

"Races" of insects (e.g., fruit flies), mice, rats, rabbits, dogs, horses, etc., have developed in this manner, and if human beings failed to develop races they would constitute the only exception in the whole biological kingdom. Between the different races within each species interbreeding is possible, even though the variations may be extreme, as, for example, among different breeds of dogs and horses. The possibility of interbreeding is evidence, among humans as elsewhere, of unity of origin, but does not indicate identity or lack of variation.

A highly important fact in connection with racial problems is that within each ethnic group there must be wide individual variations. No matter what group we consider, whether Caucasian, American Indian, Negro, or Mongolian, we will find that each member exhibits individuality; he will have his own "signatures," his own pattern of thinking, and his own set of wants and satisfactions. This makes the lumping together of all members of an ethnic group, as though they were the same, wholly unwarranted.

An inescapable point of view based upon our earlier discussions is that, inasmuch as all human beings exhibit complex *patterns* involving many items, one individual cannot be rated as generally superior and another generally inferior. They can be compared only with respect to specific items in their make-up. If there are racial *patterns*, these too cannot be called superior and inferior except with respect to single items. This leads us to the conclusion that there are no "superior" and no "inferior" races.

Cultural anthropologists in general have tended toward the acceptance of the uniformity doctrine which says that all newborn babies are essentially the same whether white, yellow, red, or black. Only the "paint jobs" differentiate one group from another. This point of view denies the existence of inborn patterns (which have substantial significance) and holds that differences between ethnic groups (except for color which might well be disregarded) are produced by culture and training. A kindred view is expressed in a recent UNESCO publication thus: "Such biological differences as exist between members of different ethnic groups have no relevance to problems of social and political organization, moral life, and communication between human beings."

The attitude which prompts such a statement as this one, e.g., the desire to promote harmony and good feeling between members of different ethnic groups, is a laudable one, which I share. But the statement itself as it stands certainly is unproved and, in the light of the material presented in this book, is probably untrue. Almost certainly biological differences *are* relevant to all of life's problems.

Our *direct* knowledge on this point is, however, inadequate. We have not studied individuals within any ethnic or cultural group enough to have definitive knowledge of their individual patterns, much less have we established ethnic patterns. On biological grounds it must be supposed that pattern differences exist between different ethnic groups. Just how important they are socially we really do not know, because the subject has not been investigated. But what investigation there has been of racial matters—limited in regard to human beings, more extensive in regard to animals—furnishes interesting material which may be used as a basis of conjecture.

A number of studies have been made with the idea of comparing Negro intelligence and white intelligence. Some unfortunately have set out to prove a preconceived conclusion either that Negroes have lower intelligence than whites or that both groups are equal. The main drawback of these studies, however, is that they did not take *patterns* into consideration. "Intelligence" was measured on the "lump of dough" theory and consisted of averaging a bushel basketful of assorted items, part of which were cultural achievements and hence meaningless insofar as native abilities are concerned. Distinctive ethnic patterns of mental capabilities have never been investigated by comparing white and Negro populations.

Biologically we know that horses, for example, not only exhibit individuality (as every horse lover recognizes) but that there are great temperamental differences between different breeds (races). Dogs exhibit the same diversity. Every pup in a litter is different from the others (and professional dog trainers recognize this) but pups from different breeds vary even more greatly. Carefully controlled breeding has made possible the existence of races of horses and dogs which are far more homogeneous than most races of men, and the differences between races, therefore, stand out more clearly.

It is possible, if sufficient effort is applied, to teach puppies from different breeds many of the same things, but all dog trainers as well as scientific investigators agree that special breeds can be more effectively trained for special purposes (pointers, retrievers, sheep dogs, watch dogs, etc.) than can dogs in general. In cases such as this, training cannot be explained solely on the basis of conditioned reflexes; the inborn make-up of the animal enters, too, and often in a striking way.

Our biological knowledge makes it seem inescapable that different ethnic groups possess inborn characteristics (aside from color) which are distinctive. It seems possible, for example, and in accord with general observation that American Indians, among whom there is wide diversity, are on the basis of inborn temperament sufficiently different from African Negroes so that slavery was feasible (and temporarily profitable) in one case and not in the other. It is a plausible suggestion, in contradiction to the White Superiority doctrine, that Negroes taken as a group are superior to whites in a number of ways: in their capacity for personal loyalty and devotion, for emotional warmth, for religion, for music, for laughter and carefreeness. This may or may not be so; the items may be poorly chosen; certainly, however, one would not pick out these characteristics as ones in which American Indians would excel.

Let us suppose for the moment that my biological interpretation is a reasonably close approximation to the true one, what then shall our attitude toward race be, and what shall we do about it?

First of all, I believe, we should learn more and more about the subject. I am confident that the truth tends to set people free and that the more knowledge and insight we have the better our attitudes will be. How can we hope to solve problems of race if we know so little of the basic facts regarding race?

I do not believe much will be gained by castigating ourselves or our ancestors for supposed stupidity, malice, selfishness, or what have you. Can we not, by taking into account all types of facts, gain an understanding of ourselves that will make possible an avoidance in the future of some of the mistakes of the past?

We need to realize, for example, that whenever groups of people live together long enough to become a "race" or a "near-race" with distinctive common characters, they develop a solidarity and a sense of belonging. This sense of *belonging* can hardly exist unless at the same time there is the sense of *excluding* outsiders. Belonging to a fraternity, service club, church, or professional society is meaningless unless someone is excluded. Even when we say we belong to the human race, we are excluding subhuman species. If we belong to a group and exclude others from it, is this not itself the basis for antagonism, and cannot it easily lead to hatred in case the outsider has characteristics and tastes different from ours?

Understanding the true situation is the best antidote for race hatred that I know of. In the fine musical show *South Pacific* there is a song which has as its theme, "You have to be taught to hate." With the purpose which lies behind this song (promoting racial harmony) I am in complete sympathy, but with the assertion I disagree, though I recognize in it a partial truth. Hatred for outsiders arises in part because of our inborn capacity and desire to belong to a group; this involves excluding; this involves failing to understand; this may easily lead to hatred. Hatred does not come about, I maintain, solely as a result of training.

As we become more and more enlightened we see more clearly the community of interests shared by the entire human race and we take less seriously our membership in smaller groups. It is hoped that we are progressing along the road toward the abolishment of much of the internal strife that besets us as human beings. Our enlightenment must include an appreciation rather than a neglect of the differences that we possess.

Current ideas held by those whose high purpose is to better race relations are often, in my opinion, of limited validity because they do not encompass the inborn characteristics that people have—only those developed by training.

In and around New York there is displayed in public places an admirable placard which states:

TRUE AMERICANS

Accept people on their individual worth regardless of their *name, color, religion,* or *occupation*

Do You?

This, endorsed by representative Catholic, Jewish, and Protestant groups, has a real appeal and much educational value. It seems, however, to oversimplify the problem, and to be somewhat unrealistic in that it appears to ask people to shut their eyes and accept as meaningless what really may be meaningful.

Someone has jokingly suggested that one way to solve the racial problem in America would be to destroy everyone's eyesight. While this would create other problems far more serious than that of race, it would end our ability to tell black from white. Surely blotting out our eyesight is not the way toward harmony. We must approach the problem with our eyes open; we must recognize differences and still develop harmonious relations.

Quite aside from its relation to the race problem, accepting people "on their individual worth" is an important though difficultly realized ideal. A severe limitation arises from the fact that we have such poor means of judging individual worth and that often, outside the realm of race relations, we depend upon superficialities. Basically, disregarding color in human relations is like disregarding other information gained by the senses: size, body build, facial features, gracefulness or its opposite, quality of voice, aroma, mannerisms.

It seems only remotely possible we will become enlightened enough to regard a man of very small stature (if he has given us no preproof of his strength) as on a plane of complete equality with a man who is large and well-built. Is it possible that a college girl who is obese will some day be considered to be as desirable sorority material as one who is slender and petite? Is it possible that enlightened males will some day disregard looks and give homely girls an equal break with pretty ones, judging them solely on their "individual worth"? All of this sounds unrealistic; it would appear that biological forces which include the utilization of all the senses are at work, and are rather compelling.

One of the interesting phenomena in connection with Negro-white relations in America is the fact, upon which authorities seem to agree, that racial crossing is definitely on the wane. Although there is a substantial amount of crossing the color line, the Negro population is tending to become more homogeneous, with less additional admixture of white blood. In connection with these phenomena all sorts of factors interplay; certainly cultural factors are important, but biological factors also operate significantly.

The biological urge to mate is, of course, very strong, especially in many males, and there is a hierarchy with respect to how this mating urge will be satisfied. According to Wright, Strandskov, and others, the tendency to pick mates on the basis of similarity of phenotype (like choosing like) has played and is playing a very important role in evolution; in mate selection top rating biologically would go to a receptive female of the same or at least closely related racial stock. Considerably farther down the rating scale would be a female of a different racial stock and of markedly contrasting appearance. Much farther down the line, but likely to come into play when other means of satisfying the sex urge are unavailable, are homosexual partners, animal contacts, etc. The existence of this hierarchy does not invalidate the high importance of conditioning, which may cause a biologically less acceptable means of satisfaction to become dominant.

Today, because of the historical slavery background of Negroes and the social effects of the white superiority doctrine, there are strong cultural bars to white-Negro marriages. Superimposed upon these, I believe, are biological factors of appearance, temperament, etc., which make such unions less desirable, other things being equal, than unions involving members of more closely related racial groups. Myrdal in his monumental study of the Negro problem in America indicates that even among those who are ardent advocates of race equality he found very few who would advocate intermarriage.

From the standpoint of what is actually happening at the present time, it seems unlikely that race amalgamation (which would be logical if the assembly-line doctrine were valid) is in the offing. Although interracial relations have manifestly improved and the slavery background of Negroes is receding into history, there appears to be no strong trend toward racial amalgamation.

Progress in interracial and other human relations will come most rapidly, I believe, if we recognize and deal with people *as they are*, acknowledging differences where they exist and making due allowances. It seems clear that each and every racial group should have equal opportunities for education, economic advance, and well-being, but that *distinctive* contributions to culture should be encouraged. It should not be required that any racial group accept and incorporate every item of the prevailing culture into its life. If, as seems to be indicated by present trends, Negroes and Indians are to remain indefinitely as separate racial groups, they should have opportunity to develop those aspects of culture which are most in accord with their genius. If individual members of a single race cannot be forced into sameness by a cultural mold, it is out of the question to force members of different races into uniformity.

The area of race relations is one in which the acceptance or nonacceptance of the uniformity doctrine is of paramount importance. Acceptance appears on the surface to be the simple solution, but it would be a solution that flies in the face of scientific facts and denies the fundamental basis for our love of freedom. Such a solution is more plausible than workable, more imaginary than real, because it involves a view of people as they are not.

XIV

Individuals and History

IT WOULD BE UNBECOMING of one who is emphatically not a historian to seek to evaluate the work of historians. On the other hand, I would be failing to develop my theme if I neglected to emphasize the importance of inborn differences as they appear to me to bear on history and a satisfactory interpretation of it. It is my opinion that no one—historian, biologist, or philosopher—has hitherto appreciated how important individuality is in human affairs. A great many, of course, have recognized the principle of variability and many have recognized that individuality is highly important. But my thought is that it is even more important than the most ardent advocates would indicate.

I am singling out history as a subject of peculiar importance because it encompasses all human affairs: political, military, scientific, artistic, religious, literary, etc. Robinson has said it concerns "all we know about everything man has ever done or thought or hoped or felt."

Though they perhaps do not say so emphatically enough, historians are aware of the fact that *man*, an abstract creature, did not design the Parthenon or build Taj Mahal; *man* did not establish a Greek world empire or build Greek philosophy; *man* did not discover America or write *Hamlet; man* did not write *The Origin of Species*, discover the positive-negative nature of electricity, or formulate the universal law of gravitation or the general relativity theory. Distinctive men were crucially important in every one of these and in all other historical events.

Inborn differences have been manifest in all eras of history, not only in the leaders whose names stand out today but among the millions of leaders whose names have been forgotten and the billions who have served as followers. If people were all alike, every page of history would tell another tale from the one we know. The struggle for power, the formation of tribes and clans, the explorations, the migrations, the conquests and wars, the peaceful pursuits—constructing, commerce and travel, art, literature—all these are activities in which individuals have played a dominant role. The role of individuals is such a self-evident fact that Emerson said many years ago, "All history resolves itself very easily into the biography of a few stout and earnest persons," a statement which seems an oversimplification, because history involves weak people quite as much as strong ones and frivolous men and women as well as earnest ones. It takes all kinds of people to make a world—or to make history.

If we should accept the uniformity theory, and some historians may tacitly do so, the study of history appears far simpler, since one important variable is eliminated. Men are then substantially alike and one has only to trace the effects of soil, climate, mountain ranges, waterways, etc., and how these have molded people into what they are. Adoption of the nonuniformity theory on the other hand makes any situation far more complicated, because we are then not dealing with *man*, a uniform and dependable unit, but with *men* who are strikingly nonuniform and far from predictable.

I have found more or less by accident, since I am not an avid reader of history, one bit of evidence which corroborates my idea that historians—like many biologists and others—may not be fully appreciative of the magnitude of inborn human differences. In his *Civilization on Trial* (1948), Arnold Toynbee first indicates how important it is that readers understand how he arrived at his view of history, and then he proceeds to trace in simple direct language how his view originated, and how he happened to be a historian rather than a physicist or something else. For him the matter is simple. He became a historian through the early influence of his mother, who was one; he learned from her to be a historian, just as he learned from her to drink tea. This is set forth not as *a* reason for his being a historian but as *the* reason. To make it more emphatic he asks himself, "Why did I not exactly follow my mother's cue?" The answer to this, too, is given clearly and unequivocally in terms of his schooling. History was taught to her from the European and English standpoint, his school emphasized Greco-Roman history. The implication is crystal clear that if he had been subjected to the same educational regime as she was, he would have had exactly the same viewpoint as hers.

It is most surprising in this mid-twentieth century that a man of Toynbee's standing and reputation could utterly ignore the possibility that heredity could have anything to do with his leanings, and yet have his glaring error unchallenged (so far as I know) by any of his contemporaries who have similar interests. This, to my mind, shows how easy it is to "get by" in the present age with a tacit acceptance of the uniformity doctrine.

As an indication that Toynbee's apparent acceptance of the uniformity doctrine is not as deep seated as one might suppose, it should be said that his whole philosophy of history appears to be in direct contradiction to the assembly-line doctrine which he seems to accept unquestioningly in the discussion of his own career. According to him society is a "field of action" but the source of all action is in the individuals composing it. Growth of civilizations is, according to this leading historical philosopher, dependent upon the timely emergence of creative personalities, and the disintegration of a society can be arrested only by the leadership of inspired individuals who act as "saviors."

Where do these *creative personalities* and *inspired* individuals come from? Were they *trained* to be inspired and creative by their mothers and fathers? If so, why did not the fathers or mothers perform the "savior" functions themselves? Clearly history cannot be interpreted along the lines of Toynbee's thinking without recognizing the existence of individuals who have within them—inborn—potentialities for great leadership.

To me, the study of history needs, as civilization needs, a far better understanding of inborn differences, both with respect to individuals and also in connection with racial characteristics. To extend Robinson's definition: History is all that we know about everything that *societies* and *individual men and women* have ever done, thought, hoped, or felt.

It is essential from the standpoint both of realism and of our liberty-loving ideals that history be interpreted and taught to our youth on the basis of the nonuniformity which is so clearly present in the human family. As we learn more and more about the play of inborn factors in human life, this aspect of history will be more clearly emphasized.

XV

Mad Hatter's Ball

Senator Paul Douglas has recently written, "If we Americans could ever stop being so mad at one another, there is just a chance that we might accomplish great things together." He had in mind particularly the then current international situation in the Far East when we fell into a "fratricidal frenzy" even when the basic questions at stake merely involved the *methods* for accomplishing the ends we all desired.

The failing to which Senator Douglas points has widespread ramifications and applies to many areas besides the political one he had specifically in mind. In many other fields we seem to get all set for being mad, like the backwoodsman who when asked how he felt on a particular public issue replied, "I ain't quite made up my mind yet, but when I do, I'm going to be plenty bitter about it."

Even in the field of religion where all parties are seeking the same Higher Power, the hatreds and suspicions which abound are tremendous and hold people of good will apart and keep them from working together for the world's betterment. How different it would be if religious people of all sects cooperated on all items on which they agree. But no! Distrust which sometimes turns into hatred keeps them apart. A similar situation pertains in our attempts to attain international peace. We may join some organization which has its own way of working toward the urgently desired end; unfortunately, however, one organization which looks toward peace tends to knife other movements because they approach the same objective from the "wrong" angle. I suppose there is enough hatred among the numerous organizations for the promotion of peace to start a war!

In the field of maintaining health we develop plenty of suspicion and hatred. Orthodox physicians have a strict code of ethics which prevents them from openly scrapping with one another, but there are numerous ways of approaching the problems of health and disease which are not under the control of practicing physicians. Public health officers, for example, belong in a different category, and often feelings are not entirely cordial between them and other physicians. Osteopaths are often tolerated by the regular medical profession, but they and the regular physicians are not in a position to learn from each other. Chiropractors, who have less training, as well as the numerous healing cults, are of course pretty much by themselves. Every group is hedged about by the suspicion of every other group in spite of the fact that all, including the regular physicians, have as their purpose the maintenance of health and the selling of services to that end. Different groups are sufficiently insulated from each other that even well-informed people find it necessary to do some of their medical shopping outside the regular channels. Many such patients feel, and I suspect that some regular physicians secretly agree with them, that anyone who goes to see a regular physician about a backache should instead see a psychiatrist about his mind! And yet backache and bellyache should logically be treated under the same supervision.

In the field of mental health and disease, there are physiological psychiatrists, clinical psychologists, "talking" psychiatrists, psychoanalysts, etc., all more or less at war with each other. Each group thinks the others are using a "wrong approach," and may hate them for it, though all are working toward a common end.

When it comes to dealing with a specific bodily organ such as the eye, or even with specific diseases, hatreds are likely to develop between one and another of those groups which seek to arrive at the same result by different means. There are the oculists *vs.* the optometrists; the followers of Sister Kenny *vs.* the "Anti's" in the treatment of polio. I was asked recently to join a national board for the study of a relatively rare disease and found out shortly that there were two boards, more or less at war with each other. In the field of alcoholism, several years ago, I found a mild war going on between two groups each with its own program and ideas.

In none of these fields—politics, religion, peace, medicine, as well as others—can we ever expect to find total agreement. As long as people think, they will differ from each other, not only on minor matters but on those of major concern. We should not hope to abolish disagreement but we can hope to diminish disagreeableness. Disagreement is natural and healthy and has a firm biological basis in our distinctive mental patterns. The real problem is how we can continue our disagreement (which we will do regardless) and at the same time shun the bitterness which stands in the way of cooperation.

It seems at times that people cherish anger as a prime prerogative and source of satisfaction. They appear to enjoy being mad at someone; if they can find no one to be mad at, they are unhappy. Whether this is the actual state of affairs in anyone's inner self is debatable, but in any event we need to understand the apparent malady.

The damage which hate does cuts in both directions; it is ruinous to the individual life of the person who hates, and is a disruptive force in the society in which he moves. A person who lives on hate, if such there be, is truly "possessed of the devil," and there can be nothing more devilish than stirring up and fostering hatred between members of the human family.

Hatred can take unto itself pious robes. One can think himself quite above hating Negroes, for example, and yet keep alive a burning hatred for people whose interracial attitudes are different from his. The poison of hate is still at work.

I suppose we might say that if there is anyone in the world who deserves to be hated it is the criminals—those who murder and steal, wholesale and retail. Actually, however, it is just as foolish to waste our energies and poison ourselves by hating criminals as it is to hate anyone else. Do effective law enforcement agents and criminal investigators, whether local or F.B.I., waste energy on hating? No! They learn to outwit criminals, to apprehend them and protect society from them. The less hatred that enters into the situation, the better for all concerned. Successful penologists do not hate their charges either.

If it is wasted effort and worse to hate criminals, how much more foolish it is to hate a fellow citizen who happens to belong to a different party, or a different wing of our party, when actually he is interested in the same ends as we are but wants to approach them by a different route. Yet this is common practice. If we could find a way to get rid of this hatred or a substantial part of it, our effectiveness in the field of politics could be increased many fold.

I remember hearing a man, in spite of his extensive "education," fairly blubber with anger, if not rage, at the mention of General MacArthur's name. It was evident that he was poisoning himself with hatred, and it interested me to know what was back of it. Did he know MacArthur personally? No. Did he have friends who knew him? No. Had he ever seen him? No. But he assured me that he had read and was well informed about him. He knew that he was no good—a self-seeker and an actor.

That General MacArthur has histrionic ability and exhibits it on various occasions no one can deny. Is this a cause for hatred? Do we not have schools to teach dramatics and does anyone imagine that all acting is carried on before footlights? Possibly MacArthur has violated what we consider good taste, but must we impose our tastes on him and hate him if he doesn't comply?

Self-seeking, if a failing, is common to all of us whether we admit it or not. Whether General MacArthur has an overabundance of this quality is something which, I believe, cannot possibly be ascertained by reading newspaper and magazine reports. Human insight and human testimony are entirely too fallible to make such judgments possible. Even if we were certain that the General cared not one whit for anything except his own personal comfort, it still wouldn't do any good to hate him.

As soon as we begin to hate anyone we "go blind" to every sensible idea which may come from that source. We can't afford to go blind to ideas. A famous name-calling indulged in by a Chief Executive has probably not faded from our memory. It is a revelation of an attitude which is far too common. It is interesting to consider precisely what is meant when we call someone an S.O.B. Does it mean literally that the individual is considered to be the male offspring of a female dog? Certainly not. Does it mean that the person so designated is judged actually to be sub-human? I believe not. When used seriously (sometimes it is used almost as a term of endearment), the appellation merely says in a not very elegant way, "I hate you!" It is an admission of frustration, blindness, and the inability to formulate or convey an intelligent idea.

The number of times that this appellation is used, or that the attitude back of it is felt, is appalling: Poor men apply it to rich men and vice versa; capitalists apply it to labor leaders and vice versa; railroad men apply it to truckers, and vice versa; pedestrians apply it to motorists and vice versa; motorists apply it to truck drivers and vice versa; voters apply it to politicians and, secretly, vice versa; public men apply it to newspaper men and vice versa—on and on.

Psychologist George Zipf of Harvard has recently suggested how much would be gained if we looked upon the behavior of fellow human beings just as we would any other natural phenomenon in the universe, such as the social behavior of insects or the nest-building activities of birds. These other phenomena we can look at and study as interesting activities without getting mad, but when our fellow human beings act in an interesting fashion, or even uninterestingly, we are likely to get as mad as hops.

Here I believe we are close to the essential idea which this chapter offers. *If* we could understand the diversity of people's tastes and wants —physical, esthetic, emotional, intellectual—we could see and study our fellow men in action, and even though their course of action might be entirely different from ours, yet *we wouldn't get mad.*

I would not disparage—far from it—the efforts of religion to build loving attitudes in human hearts. I do believe, however—and this belief rests upon an extended and careful consideration which is sympathetic to religion—that *these attitudes cannot be successfully developed unless human diversity is understood.*

I remember when I was a school child, we sang a song which was distinctive for its repetitiousness, "Kind words can never die, never die, never die; kind words can never die . . ." over and over. The sentiment of this song is superb, but admonition, even repeated often, is not enough. People must *feel* kindly toward each other, and this, I believe, is not consistently possible as long as they fail utterly to understand how diverse human beings can be—in their sensory reactions, in their tastes, in their abilities, in their ways of doing things, in their manner of thinking, in the ways they get satisfaction out of life.

If we understood this diversity we would realize what a waste of precious energy is involved in hating General MacArthur, Drew Pearson, Frank Sinatra, Leo Durocher, or anyone else. We will look upon these fellow human beings as interesting and unusual specimens; we will raise them to the nonhated level, where we know, in our sober moments, even criminals belong. We will still prefer our own ways of doing things, but we will recognize the valid existence of other ways, and will not allow anger to blind us to ideas.

I once heard a powerful sermon preached by a leading Quaker minister, who surprisingly took as his topic, "Progress can come only through conflict." The conflict which he advocated turned out to be a *conflict of ideas*. He developed his theme beautifully to demonstrate historically how conflict of ideas had always been the basis of human advance and how war, which is anathema to Quakers as well as others, *prevents* the conflict of ideas. He may well have said, though I do not remember, that hate always stands in the way of progress, too, because it blinds us to ideas. Can you imagine two people hatefully calling each other S.O.B.'s and at the same time exchanging *ideas?*

A few years ago, Professor Sorokin, Harvard sociologist, set up a research center to explore for a better understanding of hate and its origin, so that society might cut down on the production of hate. This is a most worthy purpose and merits far more support than it is likely to get. Such an objective should be approached from every angle including the biological one. It is my belief that human diversity, *coupled with a failure to understand the diversity*, is one of the prime reasons for the existence of hate. Emerson is quoted in an earlier chapter as saying, "Men lose their tempers in defending their tastes," and "The only sin we never forgive in each other is difference of opinion."

Let us consider by way of illustration as trivial an item of taste as we can think of. Suppose I thoroughly dislike pepper in my food. Could this by any stretch of the imagination be the basis for my hating someone who *likes* pepper? Not unless someone else tries to impose his or her taste upon me; then I might be annoyed at the first offense, angry at the second, perhaps even hateful if the attempts persisted. Actually people commonly do try to impose their tastes upon others (not often with respect to pepper perhaps), and the more thoroughly they accept the assembly-line doctrine of human nature, the surer they are that tastes are mere habits which can be changed at will and can therefore be imposed.

The fact that people's tastes are distinctive and to a degree innate and that they encompass hundreds of items—gustatory, olfactory, esthetic, emotional, and intellectual—coupled with the above-mentioned belief in the complete changeability of tastes and tendency to impose our tastes upon others, is enough to account for a tremendous mass of the hatred and ill will which exists in the world.

Suppose that I, like most people, have a number of dislikes. I dislike tobacco, limburger cheese, jazz music, bridge, philosophical discussions, and yakity-yak. I prefer to sit quietly in the evenings reading. (These selected dislikes are purely imaginary.) Can one imagine a better environment for building up hate in me than that I be closely associated with a believer and practicer of the assembly-line doctrine, who smokes a strong pipe, loves limburger cheese, jazz music, and bridge, and likes to talk endlessly about philosophy as well as about nothing in particular?

If, however, this imaginary person and I both recognize the inherent biological variability of human specimens, we will contrive to avoid rubbing each other's sore spots by not associating too closely. We will easily avoid hate, and if we have a common ground, in politics for example, there will be no obstacles in the way of our cooperation in that field. In a real and practical sense we will understand each other and may have a real admiration for each other's good qualities.

It is in the intellectual field that we find disparity of tastes particularly important. In a world which too often tacitly accepts the assembly-line doctrine, this disparity is the source of an inestimable amount of suspicion, ill will, and hatred. Emerson was voicing a truth when he said we never forgive each other for a difference of opinion. When in an argument one hears his opponent say, "I can't see it your way," this is taken too often to mean that the opponent is obtuse; he *won't* see it our way. If, however, we were imbued with the point of view that our minds develop according to different patterns, we would realize that people often *cannot* think alike even if they were sincerely to try.

The diversity of men's minds, coupled with the tacit ignoring of this diversity, is a fundamental basis of hatred; this fact in my opinion is of world-shaking importance. People do not have inborn hatred. Hate must be provoked. Nothing is a more effective stimulus to hate than the continual imposition of someone else's contrary taste, and nothing leads to this imposition as effectively as a belief that human beings are all alike and that tastes can always be changed at will.

There have been people who have accepted the Christian principle of good will to such an extent that they refuse to hate. When such believe in the assembly-line doctrine, what results? They must be continually perplexed, confused, and frustrated. People all around them are doing such inexplicable things—things that seem to call for hatred, yet hate is barred. Under these conditions it is difficult to maintain one's integrity. The world is out of joint and will not be righted. I believe the number of intelligent people who are in this state of frustration is large. Some can take it but others crack up under the strain.

I should think that clergymen, priests, rabbis, and religious leaders in general would live in a continual state of frustration if they have a vital belief in their religious doctrines and at the same time tend to accept the assembly-line doctrine. To a firm believer in the tenets of the traditional Protestant gospel, for example, who has the assembly-line point of view, it must be frustrating to come in contact with the vast majority of people, who pay so little attention to the religious truths which to him seem so certain.

Reformers and would-be reformers, and educators too, must of necessity be frustrated if they contact a fair sampling of the human population, and at the same time adhere to the assembly-line doctrine. Proposals and ideas which seem unquestionably valid and clearly acceptable to some of their listeners seem invalid and unacceptable to others. How can this be in a rational world, where all minds, according to the uniformity doctrine, are supposed to work the same?

Some ministers, priests, rabbis, reformers, and educators, avoid frustration by associating continually, or as nearly so as possible, with people who believe about as they do. Thus the ministers talk only to their faithful flocks and the educators only to those who elect their classes, thereby escaping the bewilderment which would arise if they were forced to deal with the general population.

I suggest that the most effective way to avoid frustration is to accept the biological fact of the diversity of men's minds. The minister or the priest or the rabbi or the teacher who does so is in a position to understand why everyone does not immediately embrace his ideas. If he is sincerely interested in his mission, he will continually seek to influence and help people; he will seek to diversify his approach in the hope of reaching more; he will recognize his own limitations and that he does not possess all truth. He can then maintain his basic convictions and be at peace with himself; the whole world will cease to be out of joint and he will not need to hedge himself about with a selected group of close sympathizers who are continually nodding their heads in approval.

Related to our problem of hate, but also involving other considerations, is the question of what our attitude should be toward the Communists of Soviet Russia, the avowed Communists in our country, and toward those who are, or are suspected of being, fellow travelers. Can we afford to be tolerant of all of them and allow them to proceed with their work unmolested and unhampered? Emphatically, no. Should we on the other hand hate them? My answer is an equally emphatic no, not because we can tolerate a loss of freedom, but because we can work against them, uproot their work, and save most effectively what we have in the way of freedom if we keep cool heads and tempers.

The question has been in the minds and on the lips of many Americans in recent years, "How could an educated young American become inclined toward Communism?" This to my mind is the kind of question which we need to ask, not in a rhetorical fashion, but with the idea of finding an adequate answer. Let's look at the budding Communists as interesting human specimens and try to find, dispassionately, why they are as they are. This is an important first step, and nothing could be more valuable to us who are opponents of Communistic ideas than understanding what motivates the proponents of these ideas. I'm sure some people have a most unwholesome fear of Communism—a fear that if they understand it they will be attracted to it. I hope that the readers of this book will come to see that for them such a fear is without foundation.

I can lay no claim to having had extensive experience with young people who are Communistically inclined. My thoughts on the subject of why they become so are for the most part closely related to the theme of this book, which I believe brings to light reasons that have not been duly considered before.

The most important of these reasons pertains to education. Young Americans have not been taught in a thoroughgoing fashion the basic principles of individuality which underlie our love of freedom and our appreciation of individual worth. Instead, they have been indoctrinated, most often by implication, with the concept of uniformity, which, followed to its conclusion, denies the value of freedom and rejects the validity of individual worth.

There is no use mincing words: Our American universities have, by wide tacit acceptance of the uniformity doctrine and its application to the social fields, failed to promote democracy effectively. This acceptance has played into the hands of those who would impose regimentation, whether originating in a Nazi or a Communist type of government. The uniformity doctrine is in accord with Communistic thinking and is basically completely out of line with liberty-loving democracy and its emphasis on individual worth. The acceptance of the uniformity idea, which has often been done vaguely without facing the implications, has undoubtedly much to do with the fear mentioned earlier, namely that to understand Communism might lead to its acceptance.

It is obvious to me that this fundamental contradiction between the uniformity doctrine (which we have repeatedly said is *tacitly* accepted more often than openly avowed) and the ideas of freedom and individual worth, is one which has never occurred to most scholars in the fields of social science. They try to accept both ideas, not realizing that they are as incompatible as snowflakes and a summer day in Texas. Anyone who loves and cherishes liberty and individual worth thereby affirms, whether he does so verbally or not, the validity of the nonuniformity theory. It is my belief that an out-and-out acceptance of the nonuniformity idea by social scientists would not only make possible tremendous advances in this field but would greatly strengthen and deepen the belief of many of the scholars in the essential validity of traditional Americanism with its emphasis on the very things which grow out of nonuniformity.

A curiously anomalous reason which I am sure underlies the attraction Communism has for some people is the desire to be *different*. This is, of course, related to the theme of this book. Differentness is exactly the thing that Communism prohibits, and precisely the quality that liberty loving democracy should permit and even promote, and yet people have in some instances abandoned American traditions for Communism partly to be different! The tendency of some people to conform to prevalent habits and customs is strong. In others the tendency to be nonconformists is very powerful. One way to be different in America is to be a Communist, and some have chosen that way. If these individuals were shipped to a Communist country, they would find that differentness is not encouraged, and they would long for the land of freedom.

Another basic reason for the lure of Communism to some young people is not so closely related to our theme. Communism purports to be humanitarian in purpose. It promises to give things to the underdog and make everybody happy. I believe we often underestimate the altruistic urge which motivates many young people. In spite of appearances to the contrary, they are often deeply concerned with the world's problems; they are touched by poverty, hunger, and disease and are perfectly sincere in their desire to see something done about it. The fact that they toy with the idea of Communism as a way out does not impair their motive. If they accept Communism, it is partly because the background of their thinking is too full of the uniformity doctrine. The error may be intellectual, not moral.

Actually, of course, Communism has never demonstrated itself as a way to help the underdog. It will not show itself and the outcome of its regime to the rest of the world for judgment. Since Communism is built upon a concept of human beings as they are *not*, I have not the slightest belief that it will ever demonstrate its applicability for solving the problem of human betterment.

Regardless of what reasons may underlie anyone's acceptance of Communism (and the reasons may be quite diverse for different individuals), it is important that we comprehend these reasons as adequately as possible. Hating Communists is no good; overcoming them, surpassing them, outwitting them, outbuilding them (in every productive way) are the important objectives. But surpassing, overcoming, and outwitting involve understanding them, and to do this we must have our eyesight and not be blinded by anger. Whether we are dealing with Communists or others, understanding and hatred are as opposed to each other as daylight and dark.

XVI

Telling Them Off

LACK OF INSIGHT into human differences can easily be the groundwork, as we have noted in the previous chapter, for the development of anger and hatred. Sometimes, however, this lack of insight makes it easy to lapse into quite a different attitude—a feeling of superiority and condescension, based upon the supposition that because other people do not think as we do they are stupid. Instead of the s.o.b. appellation we may call our fellow human beings stupid asses or nitwits (or think of them so) and the fact that we are seemingly honest in our beliefs does not make our attitude any less mistaken or less devastating in its effect. This attitude is no doubt cherished by some, because it bolsters their egos to be able to look down at so many of their fellows.

To get amusement out of the antics of our fellow beings is one of the things that makes life attractive and I would not abolish laughing at one another. There is plenty of opportunity for this diversion because there are few people indeed who do not behave asininely at least occasionally. But soberly to regard one's fellow beings as thoroughbred asses, dimwits, and generally stupid creatures, when they are guilty only of possessing individual patterns of mentality, is highly destructive of human value and stands in the way of concord. Our democratic ideals could be completely undermined if this attitude were carried to its extreme.

Many examples can be cited—some trivial and some more weighty—to indicate how prevalent this unfortunate attitude is. It is often exemplified by the attitudes that academic people and those in the work-a-day business world have for each other. Academic people often accept the lump-of-dough concept of intelligence, and are sure that they possess big lumps of this highly prized commodity. They have their Ph.D.'s and their Phi Beta Kappa keys to prove it. It is natural on the basis of the current lump-of-dough concept that they should look down from their intellectual height upon the business man who may be assumed to have only a small lump, since he has no insignia to denote otherwise. They find it merely extraneous that the business man is successful; he is just one of those on whom good fortune has inadvertently smiled. The business man, not knowing what else to do, may outwardly accept the verdict and admit that he is not very smart, but inwardly he knows better. He knows that if he is not endowed with a yen for academic work he has something else that serves his purposes better. He may, and often does, regard his academic contemporaries as "learned asses."

In the light of the truly diverse nature of intelligence, we need to revise these attitudes. "Lesson getting" very probably requires one type of mental operations and skill in practical affairs quite another. The best lesson getter may turn out to be the biggest "boob" in the world of business, or he may be totally inept in his human contacts even in an academic atmosphere. Men or women who excel in one field or another are not asses or dimwits merely because there are other areas in which they do not excel. They are human beings with natural limitations.

I have to be amused by the readiness, often found among academic people, to sound forth and criticize others about whose work they know almost nothing. I have heard those who are without theatrical experience of any kind expound with great certainty and vehemence on just how movies should be produced and distributed. Others who probably are not able to keep their own meager accounts straight may be quite certain that they know how banks should be run.

A relatively trivial example illustrates this attitude further. In my home town there is a lengthy, four-lane boulevard which for a distance follows a ravine, running through the center of a residential district. This boulevard follows, to a certain extent, the lay of the land, and is not banked on the turns in the same manner as an intercity highway would be. The speed limit on this particular boulevard is plainly marked at 35 miles per hour.

I have heard supposedly wise persons take, with considerable vehemence, two opposing positions on the matter. One violently criticized the bald-faced asses (known as engineers) for not building the boulevard like a highway capable of handling 60 mile an hour traffic. The other objected strenuously to having the speed limit on this particular boulevard raised to 35 miles per hour, and assified the councilmen who permitted it!

If such an attitude as this were exhibited only in harmless discussions with respect to such topics as speed limits, highway construction, producing movies, or operating banks, it would not perhaps be so serious. But I see evidences of the same "wise" attitudes in almost every serious discussion—particularly those indulged in by the more learned people. People who know very little indeed about the subject, so it seems to me, will explain glibly how American foreign policy has erred and how if matters had been handled according to their ideas, all trouble in the Orient would have been eliminated—it is painful to me to hear such talk—or perhaps they will opine that the Arab-Jewish problem in Palestine could all be obviated by the application of a little common sense! What twaddle! These problems involve serious conflicts in human interests and it will require the combined wisdom of all the Solomons we can muster, plus more human insight than we probably possess at present, to cope with them.

Much of this type of snobbery and the free indulgence in thinking other people stupid is based upon a disregard for the variability of people's minds, including the mind of the person who does the snobbing. As long as a person adheres to the lump-of-dough concept of intelligence and is convinced that he has a big lump, he is bound to regard anyone who disagrees with him as a dolt. The more disagreement he finds, the more doltishness he thinks there is. A general appreciation of the variability of men's minds would make us aware of our own limitations and more ready to make use of the varied intelligence that we human beings collectively do possess, to tackle in a concerted way the really difficult and baffling problems that confront us in the world.

The solution of such problems requires the interplay of all types of minds as well as the consideration of the various conflicting interests which are invariably concerned. Too often in the solution of human problems we are faced with the choice of whether or not we will rob Peter to pay Paul. In the meeting of minds we must learn to recognize that *honest* disagreement may be far more prevalent than is usually assumed. Incidentally we need to distinguish between good thinking and good talking, between being dependably sound and being merely quick on the trigger.

In the whole field of politics we see ample evidence of this same malady. We are prone to indulge in ass calling with respect to our legislators, congressmen, senators, and public officials in general, whenever they do or say something contrary to our opinions. We set up election machinery which makes it impossible for a man to get a public office without spending a large amount of someone's money; then we are surprised and critical because he is the sort of man he would have to be to get the job in the prescribed manner. We have no better means for picking honest men than Diogenes had; we distrust the motives of everybody, including hordes of public-spirited people; as a result we put obstacles in the way of competent men of integrity who might run for office, and our whole political machinery creaks and groans.

I am convinced that the great majority of the members of our national legislative body are public-spirited men (at least as much so as the people who elect them), that they all have their human limitations and are subject to human pressures, and that they are *not* asses. One of our most serious troubles is that we have not developed efficient political machinery which would take account of people as they are and at the same time utilize the democratic principles which are based upon sound biology. My guess is that we can never move very far toward our ideals until we know how to choose upright men and learn to trust their *collective* wisdom, at the same time recognizing their individual fallibility. In a large and complex society a truly *representative* form of government seems to be the only answer. Actually, however, because of mutual distrust and lack of expertness in choosing whom to trust, we have tended away from representative government and toward the development of ballots that are so long that no one could possibly vote intelligently on more than ten per cent of the items.

We may think that it is disastrous, and it is, when we trust a scoundrel. It is likewise disastrous when we *distrust* upright men and continually block the honest purposes that should be the crowning glory of our democracy. We must learn how to pick those whom we should trust and to know what we can realistically expect of them in terms of collective wisdom, in spite of their individual fallibility.

The disease which involves low-rating, ridiculing, and misconstruing anybody and everybody is serious and is rampant. It is particularly unfortunate among so-called intelligent people. Among the easy targets are policemen, who are always (in some people's minds) doing ridiculously stupid things. Actually they are human just like the rest of us; they often perform magnificently. If they are not always well chosen or well enough paid or if their training is deficient, whose fault is it? If they are subject to human pressures, how are they different from the rest of us? Firemen are also the victims of slurring remarks, but they are human, too, and in general give about the service that should be expected of them. People who are not firemen merit criticism, too. On the occasion of one fire, I saw a husky volunteer helper (who probably thought *paid* firemen were saps) struggling to disconnect an ordinary steam radiator so that he could throw it out of a second-story window to save it!

It is common for the academic intelligentsia to think of military men as supreme asses. The "military mind" is often considered as almost synonymous with lack of mind. This concept goes back to the devastatingly erroneous idea that people's minds are completely molded by their environment, and that military life with its traditional giving and taking of orders makes one wholly incapable of independent thought. History both past and present, however, reveals that military men can be great men and great statesmen as well. Military men are human and have their strong points as well as their deficiencies like the rest of us.

I am not arguing against reasoned *criticism* of specific police methods or of fire protection or military methods. We need more critical examination of everything. What I am pleading against is a combination of half-cocked and presumptuous criticism—criticism that can't possibly be helpful or constructive because it completely misses the real target through utter lack of insight into human nature.

One of the most flagrant examples of ass-calling in modern times is that indulged in by the writer of *Generation of Vipers*. Since this book presents such a clear cut (and incidentally exaggerated) case of the disease which I have been talking about, I think it wise to devote a few paragraphs to a discussion of it. The fact that it has been very widely read is an indication that it is not just one man's ideas but that the attitude it reflects has found lodgment in many minds. While the book exhibits, to my mind, a prevalent disease, this does not mean that I find nothing good in it. The author's clever and corrosive attack on hypocrisy and the serious moral purpose which lies behind his writing both deserve commendation.

To illustrate how amusingly (and consistently) the book is infected with the disease, we may pick out some of the epithets and phrases which are applied to human beings: slipwitted, utter fatuity, fantastically naive, asinine, blind, puerile, infantile, smooth brain, witless, appallingly stupid, dangerously well intentioned, pompous doodles, fiddle faddle, squirting extroverts, pipsqueaks, bumpkins, bushmen, living fossils, youngsters in a day nursery, pseudoscientific quacks, travesty of wisdom, catastrophe of misguidance, the great American oaf, jerk, cluck, macaroon, half-conscious contemporary poops, grisly bun, Iowa Yut.

These various appellations and descriptive phrases (or others with similar meaning) are applied very generally, but not quite indiscriminately, to anybody and everybody and their ideas: statesmen, professors, scientists, soldiers, preachers, doctors, business men, common men, common women. It is my impression that the asininity and stupidity of human beings, especially the leaders, is emphasized far more than their viperishness or viciousness. His book might more appropriately have been called "Generation of Asses." As a "wise guy," which the author calls himself, he ridicules the inanity of practically all of his contemporaries. There is little or no exhibition of the spirit of hatred, as would be expected if he thought his contemporaries *vicious;* rather he looks upon them as infants (which indeed he calls them many times) in need of correction.

I suppose an important factor in the appeal of this type of book, both for the reader and the writer, is that it bolsters one's ego to think that he, and an understanding few, know the answers, have intelligence, and that the great bulk of the American population is made up of Iowa Yuts,

Kansas Yuts, California Yuts, etc. I wonder if there are not a good many people who actually think, "If everyone were intelligent as I am, how rapidly would the world's ills be ameliorated!"

People actually do need bolstering for their egos, and the idea that each person is a distinctive individual, never before duplicated on this planet, should help. But to regard one's self as intelligent, in contrast to most other people whom one regards as oafs, flies in the face of perhaps the most important fact considered in this book, namely, that men have mental *patterns* and one's intelligence is not like a lump of dough.

The author of *Generation of Vipers* (as well as many of his approving readers) evidently thinks that if one is *intelligent* he sees everything fair and square. He emphatically states, for example, that a person *cannot be intelligent and be anti-Semitic.* Actually, of course, an individual might be anti-Semitic (however undesirable it is to be so) and be intelligent in many, many ways. He might be a brilliant mathematician or physicist or linguist or musician or artist or poet or playwright—and still be anti-Semitic. People's minds and personalities exhibit *patterns,* and excellence in one field is no guarantee whatever of excellence in others. Being anti-Semitic is by no means exclusively an intellectual matter; emotions are involved, and one's emotions do not always have intellectual assent.

For one to be *intelligent* in the broad, sweeping sense, not only would he have to possess broad intellectual capacities, but these capacities would have to be developed. A broadly intelligent individual should have developed excellence in all branches of mathematics, in all divisions of natural science, chemistry, physics, biology, and the rest. In these fields intelligence is not demonstrated by a mere memorization of formulas, but by a grasp of principles. Our hypothetical intelligent individual should also be able to demonstrate excellence in languages, in law, in history, in economics, in philosophy and theology, as well as all types of literature, music, art, sculpture, architecture, and drama. He should be able to solve all sorts of puzzles and play expertly all sorts of nonphysical games. He should have prowess in buying and selling, in advertising and promotion, in the handling of funds, and possibly most important of all an ability to deal with people and to form value judgments.

Who is intelligent in this sweeping sense? Certainly I know of no one.

If it were possible to roll together in one man Dwight Eisenhower, Albert Schweitzer, the late Mahatma Gandhi, and Peter Debye, we should still have only a rough approximation; high intelligence in the fields of biology, art, and literature (to name a few) would still be lacking. There is an ocean of information, insight, and prowess which constitutes the world's intellectual storehouse, but no one of us can handle more than a bucketful (or perhaps a tubful). For any man to say, or think, of himself, "I am an *intelligent* man, in distinction to most of my fellows who are nonintelligent," reveals a sore lack of understanding of what people are like and what their intelligence consists of.

It is difficult to see how the author of the aforementioned book or anyone who holds similar views could have a firm belief in democracy. If practically everyone is a sap, how can we have confidence in the value of public opinion? On the other hand, however, a sane and realistic view of human intelligence which recognizes infinite varieties of mental equipment and accords to every individual a substantial degree of gumption is wholly consonant with democratic principles.

The conservation of human resources demands that we recognize the principle of inborn variability of human mental capacities and the tremendous role it plays in all our human endeavors. When we do recognize it, the way will be paved for the abolishment not only of much hatred but also of much of the intellectual snobbery which leads one to say to his neighbor, "Thou fool!"

XVII

Reversing the Tide

IN THE FOREGOING chapters we have noted the development of a uniformity theory of human nature. It is a theory which on the surface appears to accord with democracy, but which would in time undermine the very basic ideals of freedom and individual worth and render life as we know it meaningless. It is not being promulgated from the housetops; instead it is being accepted tacitly by more and more people as fact. In opposition to this theory there is the sound and *universal* principle of biological variation, which when applied to the understanding of human nature and human intelligence renders these far more intelligible. The political result of this application is that our American democratic ideals become more compelling than ever before.

The further we roam in the fields of human interest and activity, and the more deeply we delve, the more valid and important becomes the principle of human variability. Insofar as we neglect this principle, we are bound to make a botch of education; we will continue to be impotent in our attack on many diseases; we will remain intolerant in all areas; we will cultivate misunderstanding and hatred for those whom we would honor if we were not blinded by ignorance. The firm recognition and application of the principle of human variability is a *sine qua non* for the building of a lasting civilization.

In this final chapter I will outline some of the aspects of the question,

"What can be done about it and what will *we* wish to do?" I shall assume that the reactions of my readers will be varied, in keeping with the principle of human variability, but that the least that may be expected is for the great majority to recognize the desirability of knowing more about the subject, even though they may be unconvinced as to the validity of the central theme.

If all my readers could be fired up in their desire for the truth on the subject under discussion, my purpose in writing this book would have been accomplished, because no great time will elapse between our setting out to find the truth and our arrival at the answer. The questions at issue in the reception or rejection of the basic thesis of this book are fortunately not the sort which will lead to endless disputation based upon guesses and surmises. The answers are all around us in the form of new information which needs only to be sought. We can be sure within a comparatively short time, on the basis of positive or negative findings.

A healthy skepticism and a conservative adherence to the uniformity doctrine (which may itself seem a liberal one) is understandable. As a natural scientist I am entirely sympathetic with those who want overwhelming evidence. In natural science we often find that what appears at first plausibly true may turn out later on more careful examination and analysis to be basically false. I will happily go along with anyone who wants to be sure.

There will be those who will read this book and approve of the central theme, but will object to some portions and to some auxiliary ideas. It is an inevitable fact based upon the principles set forth in this book that no two people could completely agree. Nor will they in discussing a particular subject say precisely the same things. What I have to say and my way of saying it, is my *signature* as truly as is the product of my handwriting.

While I have presented an approach to human problems which seems to me irresistibly sound, this does not mean that I regard it as the only way to arrive at truth. There is no *the approach* to anything. I realize that there will be, especially for those who have pursued thoughts along wholly different lines for many years, intellectual and emotional blocks to the acceptance of a point of view that is revolutionary to their thinking.

My ideas are only human and are presented in a human and imperfect way. It is my hope that readers will be able to overlook my handwriting as it were, and grasp that which is fundamentally true. An unfortunate fact—and I have tried to bring this out in earlier discussions—is that people allow trivialities to stand in the way of understanding and cooperation. This, it seems to me, happens with alarming regularity in everyday life.

One of the saddest and most unfortunate comments which I received regarding my book *The Human Frontier* was from a prominent man who liked many things in the book but remained indifferent because he thought the term "humanics," which I had used extensively, was a terrible one! I had thought that the use of a word which is in Webster's dictionary and means exactly what I wanted it to, "study of human nature," was proper. Furthermore it is the *only* word in the dictionary which has this precise meaning, so far as I know. However, my correspondent didn't like it, and that was that. A recognition of human variability would banish such difficulties. My intelligence and my manner of expression should not be expected to be the sort that will satisfy everyone's intellectual pattern and taste perfectly.

Addressing ourselves then to the question of what can be done to arrive at a satisfactory resolution of the problem under consideration, we find perhaps first and foremost the need for more light and more truth. This we can only find by seeking.

Search and Research

Certainly one of the matters of prime importance in connection with our theme is the continual seeking for the truth—for fuller understanding and for the workable tools which we can use to build a better world. Research in the field concerned with understanding and applying the principle of human variation can and should be intensive and extensive and has a multitude of ramifications.

To those who are attracted by purely scientific aspects and what may be called more academic considerations, it will be well to point out that never in the entire history of the world has even *one* human being been studied *comprehensively*. Before modern tools of science were available, no one tried to make such a study and now that we have many tools we use them for other purposes.

Let me illustrate: In Chapter VI we reported the results of a study of ten individuals in which we found that each exhibited a pattern of life satisfactions very different from all the others and from the average. In Chapter XI we depicted fragmentary information regarding another twelve individuals, in this case having to do with their "metabolic patterns." Again each was highly distinctive. But the two studies *are not concerned with the same individuals.* The two studies were done about two years apart and the same personnel was not available for both studies. Furthermore in one of the studies it seemed very desirable to preserve the anonymity of the subjects. However, even if the individuals were the same in the two studies, the explorations would still be very far from complete. Nothing is included regarding their psychological characteristics, nothing of their medical histories and nothing of their anthropometric measurements, to mention three *major* categories. Never have ten adult individuals (nor has *one,* for that matter) been studied in a thorough way from the biochemical, psychological, medical, and anthropometric standpoints. From limited angles, yes; from a comprehensive standpoint, no.

If we were being rigorously scientific, we would realize that induction precedes deduction. No valid classification of human beings can possibly be made until we have examined carefully at least a few specimens. After making a study of the matter for a period of years, I have come to the conclusion that any *general* classification of human beings is probably not feasible anyway, but that it will be possible to classify them *with respect to specific problems,* provided we gain first a background of information regarding many individual specimens.

The tacit acceptance of the assembly-line doctrine of human nature is certainly one of the reasons no individual or group of individuals has, in the history of science, been studied intensively. If all people are like putty and their differences are merely due to the impressions made by the environment on this putty, then why bother? If we study one human being, we know them all (so say the adherents of the assembly-line doctrine); they can all be molded into the same pattern; let's understand the molding process and disregard the raw material.

One large, important, and widely encountered problem which can only be solved by research that uses human variability as a basis, is this: How far can suggestion (or psychology in the popular sense) go in modifying the lives and the health of the people? To what extent can pain, distress, trouble, and their opposites—comfort, ease, and pleasure—be psychogenic in origin?

I come upon people occasionally who seem to me to have gone hog-wild in their beliefs on this particular subject. They start out, let us say, with a harmless and undeniable fact, namely, that drinking coffee (or taking the equivalent amount of caffeine) does not keep *them* awake at night. Since this is a fact and they are accustomed to the careless habit of assuming that people are uniform, it does not seem to them a very big leap to conclude that coffee never keeps anyone awake. If anyone thinks it does, he is deluded; it is in his mind, they assert. If they are going to go this far they might as well take another "logical" step and say, "Drugs and medicines have no effect on anyone; it is all a matter of suggestion." Perhaps they would pause just this side of the idea's ultimate and avoid saying, "If you take a dose of mercuric chloride thinking it is sodium chloride, it will do you no harm, whereas if you take a pinch of salt thinking it is mercuric chloride, it will kill you."

Suggestion is doubtless a potent factor in the lives of many people, but there are strong indications that some are far more suggestible than others. How could this be otherwise in the light of all that we know about individual patterns, in the whole area of emotions, thoughts, and desires? The suggestibility of *man* has been studied, the suggestibility of *men* has received scant attention. We need to know more about this so we can recognize the limits to which suggestion is likely to go in different individuals and under particular circumstances.

A similar extreme belief often exists with respect to the relation of mind to disease, and this calls for further study and research. It is reported that certain psychiatrists have succeeded in inducing hives by building up resentment in their patients. From this, if we unconsciously accept the uniformity theory, we may conclude, "Urticaria is always caused by resentment." Let's go further and say all skin diseases are caused by some unfavorable mental state, and in view of the well-established fact that worry can contribute seriously to the development of ulcers, why limit ourselves to *skin* diseases? Why not say that all diseases are fundamentally psychogenic in origin? Further research which recognizes human variability as an important factor is needed to give insight into the perplexing problems involving the interrelationships between people's minds and their bodies.

The problem of psychogenic pain needs to be explored and understood, and this is only possible if human variability is taken into account. Some people are born completely insensitive to pain, some are extremely sensitive, and there are all gradations in between and with respect to different parts of the body. To say that a pain has its origin "in the mind," simply because we cannot easily find another origin, is dangerous. Research and study, fully recognizing inborn human variability as a potent factor, must decide about many of the mind-body relationships. Mental states can influence health and bodily functioning; likewise, it is perfectly clear that bodily states can tremendously affect mental states. How these are interrelated must be studied with real people rather than with an abstraction. Then we will have a basis for sound judgment.

For me personally one of the most compelling arguments for research in the field of human variability is based upon my conviction that such research will almost certainly provide the basis for the solution of many specific, pressing, and hitherto unsolved problems.

The problem of alcoholism, as has already been explained, has yielded in a substantial manner when it was attacked from the standpoint of biological variation. The problem of sex crimes is another one which can only be understood and attacked on the basis of knowledge about the inborn differences between people. Incidentally Kinsey's study is another case of intense investigation of many people from but one angle. Some of those who exhibited exceptional sex characteristics certainly merited intensive study from many angles, but of course the Kinsey group were not prepared to do this. It would have extended the already large project much beyond the limits of the available budget. Another specific problem which needs to be studied with biological variability in mind is that of divorce. Whether there is to be or is not to be a continual trend toward less rigid mate selection, and more freedom to correct marital mistakes (or supposed mistakes), the importance of understanding the elements in a happy marriage and thus avoiding incompatibilities remains. If marriage ties are considered sacred and inviolate, it is surely important that people who are fundamentally incompatible be not joined. If marriage ties are for better but not for worse, then the need for compatible choices is still urgent. Marriage counsellors have in many cases performed an outstanding service without utilizing more than a cursory knowledge of individual variations. They (and the parties directly concerned) can do vastly better when there has been accumulated a background of information about individual differences and their significance in the realm of marriage.

The possibility of clearing up many obscure diseases as a result of paying attention to human variability has already been mentioned. Another problem that requires the same approach is that of accidents. There are accident-prone people who have far more than their share of accidents, and at the other end of the scale there are those who have far less than their share. How human variability enters into this must be ascertained by research.

The matter of communication of ideas is one which concerns all of us and if, as has been stated in an earlier paragraph, each of us possesses a "signature" with respect to his manner of communication, it is highly important that these signatures be understood. If we bring human intellectual variability into the picture, it may make the problem of semantics and the use of words appear even more difficult, but actually, as in many other cases, the recognition of differences leads to better and easier understanding. If, for example, our observations and deductions regarding alcoholism are valid, the recognition of differences between alcoholics and others does not widen the gulf between them and other people; in fact it has made possible in some cases a complete closing of that gap.

Another broad problem, which concerns all of us both directly and indirectly, is that of finding the right job for the right person and vice versa. Many studies have been made of this and progress has been considerable, but whatever has been done could be done with far greater success if we had more insight into biological variability and the significance of the various items of difference. To me it is extremely curious that anyone could seriously entertain the uniformity idea, when it is so patently true in the field of employment—and generally recognized—that round pegs don't fit into square holes and that a round peg can't be made into a square one.

Research and investigation takes time and costs money, and the question arises as to who will do this research and who will take care of the expense. Badly as research is needed in other areas, I believe some substantial amount of the manpower can be diverted at once into the type of research which we are discussing. At first this amount may be small, but as results are forthcoming, the amount of effort pointed in this direction will grow to large proportions.

Educational institutions, large industries, private foundations both large and small, should support financially these numerous investigations. I believe this is an important area for the National Science Foundation to cultivate inasmuch as its resources should be large enough to do inclusive work of a nature which a group with relatively small funds cannot. The Ford Foundation has, in working out the five areas in which it will support investigation, indicated an interest in this field. Both Area V, which has to do with the development of a "science of man," and Area IV, which is concerned with education, specifically include human differences within their compass. It is to be hoped that some of the wealthy residents of my own state, Texas, will see the opportunity to perform a magnificent public service by supporting anywhere and everywhere, when opportunity offers, investigation directed along the lines suggested by this book.

A Break through the Iron Curtain

One of the by-products of the type of investigation which we have been discussing, particularly that research which involves physiological and biochemical study of human individuals, will be the penetration of the "Iron Curtain" by the information and the ideas involved.

In some areas of thought it is possible for the government of the U.S.S.R. to exercise censorship and keep Russian scholars and their pupils ignorant as to what is going on in the non-Soviet world. Certainly there could be no pressing demand on the part of Soviet scholars to know about the current sociological theories or opinions of American leaders in these fields, because these are based so largely upon our culture and our way of doing things. We do not demand that American scholars who take the Ph.D. degree in Social Sciences have any first-hand familiarity with current thought in other countries such as would be gleaned by reading current articles in foreign languages.

In the field of the Natural Sciences, however, the needs are very different. I can best illustrate by describing briefly the situation in chemistry, the vast field which has been my professional interest. It will be surprising to many of my readers to know that there are published, all over the world in all languages, about 10,000 scientific journals which report original chemical findings. Many of these are published weekly or monthly.

Articles from most of these journals are cited and abstracted in English in *Chemical Abstracts*, an American superpublication which has as editors, assistant editors, and abstractors, scientists to the number of about eight hundred. This biweekly journal abstracts an average of about two hundred original articles every day of the year including Sundays and holidays. No abstract journal in the chemical field seriously competes with *Chemical Abstracts* and this publication is quite indispensable for chemical workers in all lands, Soviet and non-Soviet. As these words are being written there is being distributed through this medium to all scientists throughout the world the results of the investigations on biochemical individuality referred to in Chapter XI. Whenever in the non-Soviet world there are publications of this character, they will be digested and called to the attention of Soviet scientists through the medium of *Chemical Abstracts*. This type of research material will, on the basis of our experience, contain striking and irrefutable evidence supporting the general thesis of human variability and undermining the uniformity theory on which regimentation rests. Of necessity this evidence will be so well mixed with chemical and physiological material which is absolutely essential that censorship will be impracticable.

If we delve seriously into the chemical and physiological facts which make the idea of human variation so compellingly important, there will be hundreds and thousands of articles dealing with the subject published each year. The findings can hardly fail to come to the attention of the thousands of Soviet scientists *and their pupils*, and the basic biological facts which underlie our democratic love of liberty will become known throughout the world. Here is a way to pierce the Iron Curtain which may prove to be important. We will be taking advantage of the fact that chemistry as well as a number of related sciences are completely international in scope.

Education and Re-education

As one writer has truly said, "Today it is usual for people to have an emotional bias against believing that differences between individuals are to any serious extent caused by differences in their heredity." The roots for this emotional bias may be found in our failure to appreciate that differentness or individuality is fundamental to our love of liberty and that our American traditions rest upon this foundation. When we have become educated or re-educated to see how closely individuality and love of liberty are tied together, we will, it is hoped, lose this emotional bias which has barred us from basic truth.

For some people it will be difficult and for others impossible to recast their mode of thought. The attitude which they have grown to adopt unconsciously is one of yearning to be normal and to make everyone else so at all costs. They regard the goal of human endeavor as a leveling process which might even be described as "correcting God's mistakes." If the Creator did make everyone different, they say in effect, surely we must do all we can to smooth over the irregularities and come out with a uniform product that can be counted on to be thus and so. A story has been told of a professor who, when he had compiled the arithmetical grades of his class, made the discovery that if he took away ten to twenty points from those with high grades and gave them to those with the low grades, there were grade points enough to go around; everybody would have enough to pass and everyone would be happy!

The principle of mutual aid is as valid a biological principle as is the survival of the fittest, but there are types of mutual aid (of which equal distribution of grade points is an example) that are spurious and vicious in their effects. It is a matter requiring judgment to decide when the practice of the principle, "from each according to his ability, to each according to his need," accomplishes its laudable purpose. Without making more than one allusion to the domain of taxation, it is suggestive that President Conant of Harvard once indicated that high *inheritance* taxes are in accord with the American principle of equality of opportunity, but that high *income* taxes by the same criterion appear to be fundamentally out of line with our traditions.

Before we can start teaching children the principles of individuality, we must be convinced ourselves of the value of those principles and their applicability to human life. Further research will help to bring us this conviction, and for some it will be required before the full force of the idea is felt. Actually, of course, research, education of adult teachers, and education of children—all along the lines of individuality—can take place simultaneously.

I believe that a start can be made in the primary grades or even in kindergarten to teach children that they possess individuality. Of course, ways and means must be worked out and pitfalls must be avoided, but I see no reason why even small children might not profitably learn about their differences in tastes (colors, designs, music, flowers), their differences in motor skills, their differences in hearing and in visual characteristics.

Schooling surely is for the purpose of bringing about a better adaptation between pupils and their environment. Since children are clearly not completely adaptable, it follows that they should learn not only about their environment but also about *themselves*. Any school which does not give children a better understanding of themselves as individuals would seem to be a failure. From this standpoint a superb kind of school would be one in which a student could continuously be learning more and more about his own aptitudes and potentialities. It would then be a mark of education to know one's self.

As things stand at present it is estimated that less than six per cent of the schools of the country offer even token forms of vocational guidance. This, when it is offered, is necessarily (on the basis of current ignorance of human variability) based upon wholly inadequate information.

The problem of how much attention we will pay to individuality in our schools *depends upon how important individuality is*. If its importance is even appreciable, we should spend more effort on cultivating it than we do.

There are several misapprehensions about individuality which need to be cleared up. One is illustrated by an article written by a physician and published a few years ago in *Harper's Magazine*, on the theme of the nonexistence of the average boy. The article made out an excellent case for the fact that each boy is different—so far so good—but the discussion seemed to carry the implication that when the boys grew up they got to be normal. There is abundant evidence of a deep-seated desire in some quarters to correct God's mistakes and make people alike. Actually it seems to me that the results of the experiment described in Chapter VI should be enough to convince anyone of the futility of any such attempt. Boys are different. When they grow up to be men, they are perhaps more different than ever!

An authoritative writer has indicated that, for the proponent of progressive education, "the molding of the child to the social order is the principal business of modern schooling." This "child molding," which admittedly is capable of different interpretations, certainly smacks of a desire to turn out a uniform, or at least a predetermined, product. It would perhaps take little boys and girls who are individually different and mold them into bigger boys and girls who have lost their individuality. It seems to me that a case can be made for the idea that the principal business of schooling is to *fit* rather than to *mold* children into the social order, though of course the molding activities when appropriate should not be avoided.

In certain educational institutions there has developed a considerable interest in an area designated "child growth and development." This interest may carry an implication which is contrary to the theme of this book. It does so whenever it stresses *development* to the neglect of the *starting material.* Whenever, as the result of development from babyhood, a worthy adult individual comes into being, this individual's existence is predicated by the previous existence of an infant with distinctive potentialities. If we think we can start with nothing, or with a meaningless, patternless, something, and *develop* out of it an adult human individual, we have a misconception of how development takes place. This is akin to the prevalent and easy idea that if someone's mind doesn't work the way we think it should, that is, follow our pattern, all it needs is "maturing."

Although the saying made famous by Pope, "the proper study of mankind is man," is commendable if interpreted broadly, it can and does carry an implication for some people that is unfortunate. If we imply that understanding *man*, a hypothetical abstraction, is the proper goal of human endeavor, I of course disagree most heartily. In order to avoid this implication, I would amend Pope's statement even with the sacrifice of euphony and rhyme, to make it read, "the proper study of mankind is *men*." Studying *man* has presumably occupied much of our efforts in time past; studying *men* has not received the attention it deserves.

I would also object, as I have in an earlier chapter, to the excessive use of the expression "*the* individual" and to developing too great an interest in what is essentially an abstraction. I believe it would be an aid to clear thinking if we would substitute the word "individuals" about nine-tenths of the time, when we are inclined to use the expression "the individual." We should not become interested in "*the* individual child" or "*the* infant" or in "*the* mature mind." All of these expressions carry the implication of a uniformity which does not in fact exist. Our proper interest should be in *individual children*, in *infants* and in *mature minds*.

The point of view which we have developed is subject to one other possible misapprehension which needs correction, namely that it denies the importance of environmental influences. Nothing could be farther from the truth, as I will try to make clear by a few illustrations.

Take the problem of crime and criminals, for example. Certainly no one believes more thoroughly than I do that alteration of environment can prevent crime. In my opinion thousands and millions of potentially fine members of society become criminals because their environments induce them to. Potential criminals, like the rest of us, have their distinctive patterns of desires, thoughts, and emotions, and without posing as an expert, I can say that in my opinion the vast majority of them could be saved as useful members of society if we recognized their individuality and were reasonably skillful in finding suitable outlets for their respective energies. Many potential criminals have unusual abilities; school activities often do not fit their contrasting patterns. Overwhelming evidence indicates that finding suitable occupations for individual members of society will prevent or even cure criminal tendencies.

The fact that I have been an educator most of my adult life and expect to continue work in this profession—not because it is convenient but because of a deep conviction as to its importance—should be taken as evidence of my belief in the outstanding importance of environmental influences. Not only does the proper type of education (which takes individuality into account) have great potentialities for prevention of crime, but also its possibilities are great because it can prevent a tremendous amount of frustration in frazzled minds—minds that are frazzled because they are not allowed to follow along the lines of their potentialities but instead are being forced into a crippling mold.

Another evidence of my belief in the efficacy of environmental influences is based upon my great interest in the field of nutrition. Nutrition is one of the most important environmental influences, and I suppose very few believe in its efficacy to the extent that I do. In previous chapters I have indicated how alcoholism has been attacked nutritionally and that many obscure illnesses, including a number that are classified as mental diseases, are probably ultimately capable of being successfully treated by nutritional means. In all these cases, however, inborn differences must be taken into account, and we must know more about them before we can select the environmental changes that will be effective.

Upheaval in Basic Thinking

The approach to human problems which I am advocating will necessitate an upheaval in the basic thinking of many. I am not urging a transformation in human nature. I am not reiterating the admonitions of past ages, "Be good," "Be better," or "Think and act sensibly." What I am advocating is nothing impossible or impractical.

Upheavals in thinking can come about. Centuries ago people thought in terms of an earth-centered universe; now we do not. A few decades ago we thought in terms of matter and energy as separate and indestructible entities; now we do not. Only a few years ago we thought of interatomic energy as wholly unavailable. Now we know it is not.

Much of our thinking about human problems in centuries past has been in terms of *man* and his attributes. It is my contention that biological variability is so very great and so very significant that a consideration of *man* in connection with many human problems has become obsolete. We must cease being so grandiose and so universal in our thinking. In the prehistoric gropings with respect to what we now call astronomy, it could be that someone with a philosophic or contemplative turn of mind talked to himself after this fashion, "The problem of the heavens is essentially the problem of the star. If we could know what *the star* is, we would know the secret of the heavens." By now we have moved ahead so that we know a great deal about the heavens, but we do not talk about the problem of *the star;* we talk in terms of planets, comets, asteroids, suns, nebulae, variable stars, binary stars, novae, dwarf stars, giant stars, interstellar matter, etc.

Paraphrasing the imaginary primitive astronomer, students of human problems have been prone to say, "The problem of the human race is essentially the problem of *man.* If we could know what *man* is, we would know the secret of human destiny."

Some day we shall appreciate that a multitude of the problems of the human race do not center in man, but in a population which is biologically so diverse that in connection with these problems all humanity simply cannot be lumped together. For some purposes and in connection with certain problems, lumping together may be warranted, but for other problems this relatively superficial procedure can only fail.

We speak for example of "man's inhumanity to man." I believe a careful analysis of the phenomena coming under this alleged classification will show that it is not man's inhumanity to man, but the inhumanity of specific men or groups of men to other specific men—and that differences in make-up, in interest, in mental patterns, had a very great deal to do with the inhumanity which was practiced.

In his valuable and admirable book *The Proper Study of Mankind,* Stuart Chase reveals the desire for that sweeping generalization and universality which to my mind is highly unrealistic. How is it possible, he asks, to think of a world state unless founded on universals? "Administrators of such a state must be able to recite them backward in their sleep, 'This is what all men, everywhere, since time out of mind, under such and such conditions, are prone to do.' "

When we consider the highly diverse patterns of desires revealed by the ten individuals discussed in Chapter VI, it seems utterly unthinkable that we can lump all humanity together and concentrate on "this is what *man* will always do." Though the parallel is far from perfect, the same principle would be involved if we were to approach the subject of astronomy with the attitude: "We must find out not how individual heavenly bodies or types of heavenly bodies behave; we must be able to recite backwards and forwards the essence of their universal behavior—how *all* heavenly bodies behave." I would not disparage the importance in astronomy of the law of universal gravitation, but I do affirm that this law is something that a high school student can learn and still remain quite uninitiated in the science of astronomy. If we are to be versed and competent with respect to human nature, we must know much more than merely those things that "Everyman" will do.

In the same valuable book, which contains so much excellent material that I wish I could avoid calling attention to what to me are weaknesses, Chase dwells at considerable length on an imaginary, hypothetical average character named George Rutherford Adams, whose activities and thoughts are a matter of major concern. He is "the product of a group and the culture that goes with it," and the impingement of various cultures on this prototype is interestingly and validly related as far as I am able to judge. If this individual is purely an imaginary being, he is the product of imagination and can have any characteristics the imaginer likes. If, as I suppose, he stands for a human being, then I contend that the above statement is only a partial truth and should be amended to read: "He is the product of his heredity *and* the group and the culture that go with it." This is an important amendment, since it takes much of the uniformity out of human nature and destroys much of the value of the prototype, because the inheritance of each individual is different.

It is my thought that our basic thinking will gradually undergo a change in that we will cease trying to lump all people together. Instead we will find it feasible and advantageous to classify human beings in relation to the various problems they encounter. With respect to the problem of alcoholism, for example, there are two main groups: (1) those who have no difficulty in controlling their drinking, and (2) those who have difficulty. There is possibly no *sharp* dividing line between the two groups since there are various gradations. With respect to various other problems, which will often be complicated, there is hope that investigation, which must be both extensive and intensive, will make possible the development of helpful classifications. These may be less difficult than we imagine when we actually try using modern tools and keep in mind continuously that both heredity and culture may enter into every human situation.

Many Books Must Be Rewritten

If this upheaval in basic thinking of which we have been speaking materializes (and this seems to me inevitable) it will make obsolete a vast number of books on many subjects. Books are being rendered obsolete continuously anyway but in this case the obsolescence will be on a more wholesale basis.

Let us consider first some of the books we use in educational work, starting with those dealing with biology. In the presently available books of this type, the human implications are seldom stressed, and when they are, human variability and its import are neglected. Genetic variability is a well-recognized fact in the whole biological realm, but the students go merrily on their way, oblivious to the fact that many human problems—and social ones—have their roots in the subject matter which is immediately in front of their noses. In view of the well authenticated facts and interpretations which we have presented, I do not see how anyone can in this day and age be considered educated for human living unless he or she has digested the equivalent of a good course in biology including its human implications. These human implications should not be treated as mere decorations on the cake, but should be considered seriously. Of course differences in interpretation will arise; this will add to rather than detract from the value of the study.

Next, let us consider as a group the fields of biochemistry, physiology, pharmacology, and physiological psychology, all of which are closely related to biology and find extensive applications in medicine as well as elsewhere. Books and other materials in these fields have had a strong tendency to leave human variability out of consideration. One may find book after book dealing with these fields (not so many in physiological psychology) which are otherwise excellent, but which give *no hint* as to the possible importance of human variability. The uniformity theory is tacitly accepted and deviations, if mentioned, are passed over lightly as unfortunate idiosyncrasies. The urge to make these subjects "scientific" and to stress generalizations has been too great to overcome.

Psychologists have for many years been aware of the importance of individual differences and a number of worth-while books have been written on the subject. Because of the emotional bias referred to earlier and the influence of the behavioristic school, relatively little attention has been given to the problem of the extent to which heredity is involved. There has been a fear, I presume, that such considerations would have unfortunate repercussions. The whole of the field of the psychology of individual differences needs to be extended—an inordinate amount of time is usually spent on differences between the sexes—and it needs to be related fearlessly to genetics, to physiology, to pharmacology, and to biochemistry. This will inevitably involve a recasting of thought in the whole field of psychology as has been suggested in an earlier discussion. The "psychology of individual differences" will not remain like a wart on the face of the subject of psychology, but instead the principle of human variation will permeate every area in the broad field.

When psychology has undergone this revolution and has incorporated genetic facts into its thinking along with environmental facts, the way will be paved for the development of real insight into the causes and potential treatments of mental disease. *Man* does not become insane; it is only individual men and women who become so. A survey of a large number of cases of schizophrenia by Kallman offers convincing evidence that heredity is an important predisposing factor in this disease, a conclusion which fits in with all that we know about human variability.

The fact that hereditary factors predispose in mental disorders does not by any means preclude the possibility of developing remedies or of preventing the appearance of the maladies. General recognition of individuality and the wide differences that exist would doubtless help tremendously—people may become mentally ill as a result of being forced into an ill-fitting mold. All of the shock treatments, etc., which are now used with considerable effectiveness are not ruled out by the concept of hereditary predisposition. The nutritional approach to mental disease, which has many ramifications and I believe promising potentialities, is put on a rational and workable basis only when we recognize the existence of inborn differences in nutritional needs.

It will doubtless appear presumptuous to some of my colleagues in the field if I say that many books in social science need to be rewritten to include the facts of human variability. I would, however, be neglecting a development of my theme if I did not say so.

Although there are doubtless exceptions, by and large the currently used books in the field of social science are written on the assumption that "man is a product of the culture or cultures in which he is reared." I would amend this to read, "*men* are the products of their respective heredities and of the culture or cultures in which they are reared." I would not subtract one iota from our knowledge of what cultures do, but I do think there is need for an upheaval in our social thinking in terms of a broader and more adequate understanding of why people behave the way they do.

In the field of economics, Wesley C. Mitchell as long ago as 1914 realized the inadequacy with which fellow economists analyzed the behavior of the men with whom they were concerned. He suggested that economics cease to be a system of pecuniary logic involving nonexistent conditions and become a science of human behavior. From our earlier discussions and our excursion into the domain of what men and women live by (Chapter VI), it will be obviously apparent that the concept of economic man is a highly circumscribed one and a picayunish substitute for the real people with whom economics and every other social science deals.

It is unfortunately true—it could hardly be otherwise—that the taint of the uniformity idea has invaded fictional writings, plays and movies as well as books and magazine articles intended for serious readers. I can scarcely pick up a periodical without seeing some evidence of it. It is to be hoped that there will be more and more literary works (and I see evidence of it occasionally) in which the other view—the nonuniformity idea—will be given something like its due.

Before writing the final sentence in this book I wish to testify with all candor and sincerity how valuable the ideas presented in this book have been to me personally in my attitudes toward people in general and toward individual people in particular. I wish I could go back in my past experience and resolve the antagonisms which festered unnecessarily because I lacked the human understanding that I now have. As a result of explorations in this field, I find people more interesting than before; I find it very easy to like them and to have a genuine appreciation of their worth even when they are constituted very differently from me. I have come to regard many of them as very interesting and oft-times perplexing specimens, but not unworthy of my respect and my affection. I firmly believe that if I had been taught from childhood more about individuality (and my mother was more aware of individual differences than most), my whole life would have been materially happier and more satisfying, I would have had greater peace of mind, and my productivity would have improved both as to quantity and quality.

Finally I wish to say that my central purpose in writing this book has been to stimulate the search for truth, along lines which seem to me to be compelling. I do not claim to "have the answers," nor do I assume that the truth will turn out precisely in accordance with my expectations. I hope that few readers will, after reading my thoughts as set down, be inclined to contradict them without a reasonable test of their validity. I dare to hope that on the basis of careful examination, the uniformity idea with all of its connotations will gradually become discredited and discarded and that the ultimate acceptance of the nonuniformity idea will greatly strengthen our love of liberty and foster wholesome human relations. If this hope is realized, we will be able to perform further wonders by environmental control, and will be pioneering toward the development of a science of human understanding. Only in this way can we insure that "government of the people, by the people, and for the people shall not perish from the earth."

Index